Rescuing Barbara

Rescuing Barbara

Cass J. McMain

Holland House

www.hhousebooks.com

Paperback ISBN: 978-1-910688-40-3

Cover design by Ken Dawson Creative Covers
Typeset by Polgarus Studio

Published in the UK

Holland House Books
Holland House
47 Greenham Road
Newbury, Berkshire RG14 7HY
United Kingdom

www.hhousebooks.com

For somebody that I used to know.

SECRET TREASURE

My mother had extensive bridgework in her mouth, all gold. She could use her tongue to unhook it and flash it at me. The first time she did that for my amusement, she told me she was a pirate. I was four, five years old. She said she had priceless gold pirate treasure hidden in her mouth and asked if I wanted to see it. Then she opened her mouth and flashed it at me, absolutely blowing my mind. I'd beg her, after that, on a daily basis: Be a pirate! Show me your gold! Show me your gold! After a while she said it wasn't good to do that because it would mess up her teeth. She flashed her gold at me only rarely then, when she was in a very good mood. "Yarr," she would say, making a hook with her finger. "Yarrr, I'm a pirate." She said not to tell anyone else she had it, that it was her secret pirate treasure, quite valuable. She said the people might steal it if they knew.

As a child, I worshipped her. We used to be quite close. She was really a terrible mother, but we had things in common, she and I. We had the same eyes and the same sense of humor. We had all the things people have when they know each other very, very well. The insider info. The pirate treasure.

Then she moved away. She moved very far away with

almost no warning, and after that we had only letters and bad phone calls. And then there were no letters and there were worse phone calls.

And then there was nothing. I went from being an insider to being nobody, nobody at all.

When she was a pirate, she told me that when she died, I could sell her gold and become rich. In the end, though, there was no treasure left. Gold nor teeth.

THE ART OF
LOOKING PENSIVE

Write what you know, they tell me. Write for yourself, not for an audience. My varied writing groups have lots of advice, for better or worse. Sell the sizzle, not the steak, they say. Be yourself, they say. Then they say: be mysterious. The author photo should definitely be done by a pro, they tell me. But I can't afford that.

I pose in front of the Clematis. My husband snaps a few pictures. He tells me to smile. But I don't want to smile. I want to look thoughtful. I'm a writer, an artist. I want to look pensive. *Click, click*, he takes more photos. They are terrible, but my husband is losing patience with this project. He wants to call it finished. You look fine, he says. Good enough, he says. It's just a *picture*, he says.

You don't understand, I tell him. I need to pique people's interest in me. I should look pained, dammit, I should look intelligent and misunderstood and *tormented*. He rolls his eyes at me, takes a deep breath, has an inspiration. He smiles.

Think about your *mother*, he says. And... *Click*.

It's perfect. I look not merely thoughtful and pensive. In this picture I look positively haunted. I almost don't recognize myself. I stare at the haunted woman and have a sad, angry laughing fit.

It will be another week before I get the first phone call. The first of the last phone calls.

Start the story where the story starts, my writing group tells me.

Good luck with that.

TANSY

Our house was a handmade thing. It had been horse stables. My father added on, built it all from adobe, brick by brick, himself. My uncle Bob helped, too. I have pictures of both of them slaving away, Bob barely grown, thin as Slenderman. I was told – by my mother – that she helped a great deal also, that it was a labor of love. I have pictures of her, sitting on the mud bricks and smoking cigarettes. I doubt she lifted a pretty finger, really. Perhaps she mixed drinks and offered words of encouragement.

When it was finished, it was a long, thin house. In the middle of nowhere, nestled in the Bosque, surrounded by ditch banks. They call them aquecias now, but they were ditches then. Children were told the legend of La Llorona. Ditches are deadly, after all. Ditches are deadly, stay away.

To the stables, my father had added on a nice master bedroom that had a doorway into the front yard, and a long, long hallway with a small window looking out on the back ditch where we burned our trash. The neighbors broke in through that small window and stole from us; my mother saw them sitting out there when we came home. As we had no proof, nothing was done. We replaced the small window with one that had reinforcement so it couldn't be broken. Then they broke in the front. (Hacked down our beautiful hand-carved front door with an axe, the brain-dead swamp monsters.) They stole all my mother's jewelry. They stole all our saddles, too, which we had brought in the house to prevent their theft from the barn. They even stole my little saddle, and my parents didn't bother replacing it. They sold my horse instead.

Anyway, because of all this theft, my mother wanted our young dog, a fine German Shepherd named Tansy, trained as a guard dog. The trainers made her go through obedience training classes first. Every week, for months, we made the long drive to the heights, to Acoma Training Center. A man named Bill Dooley taught Tansy to sit, stay, lie down. I would wait in the bleachers, drawing or reading. Watching all the dogs sit, stay, lie down. After the class, my parents would usually go out for coffee with Bill Dooley and his wife, and they would talk late into the evening. Once Tansy had her certificate of obedience, they put her through the guard dog training. I watched Mr. Dooley teach her to guard and attack for several more weeks, with his burly assistant and his padded arm. "Watch him, Tansy! Watch him." They continued to go out for coffee afterwards with the Dooleys, who had become close friends. We always came home late.

Once Tansy was fully trained for guard-dogging, my mother felt better, safer. But she wanted to test it out, so one day on the spur of the moment, she decided to dress up like a burglar and pretend to break into the house. She told me she would come in the side door of the master bedroom and pretend to be ransacking the place, and I was to call for Tansy and tell her to "watch him, Tansy!" When I called Tansy, she was going to stand by the bedroom door listening for her to come down the hall. She said she would be relying on me to tell her when Tansy was coming or if she wasn't, because she was afraid if she opened the door the dog might overpower her and attack – which she had been trained to do.

So she put on one of my dad's big coats and a hat, and wrapped her face in a bandana à la Jesse James, put on some sunglasses. She hulked around in the yard making manly groaning noises and then pretended to break in the side door. (Really, knowing now what I do know about dogs, I seriously doubt for a moment that the dog didn't know exactly who that was.)

Nevertheless, I called Tansy, and she, being a Good Dog (and a highly-trained one), came immediately from the other end of the long, thin house to attack the intruder. My mother asked if the dog was coming, and I said yes, she is coming. But my mother apparently didn't believe me, because she asked again and stuck her fool head out the door to see. She's coming! I shrieked, she's coming! Get back, close the door! My mother panicked when she saw the dog trotting down the long hallway, jumped backwards and snapped a tendon in her leg. She barely got the door closed in time. She was in a cast for months. We never called on Tansy as an attack animal again, either in jest or for real. So that was the end of that.

However, word did get around about the fact we had a trained attack dog, and the neighbors didn't break into the house again for a while. Scum neighbors; I wish Tansy had torn them limb from limb, but she was never given the chance.

When we came home late from those dog training sessions, I always pretended to have fallen asleep in the car, so my dad would carry me to bed.

I loved that part.

RESCUING BARBARA

It's the spring of 2012, and my husband and I are driving to North Carolina. We're going because of a phone call from a friend of my mother's. A plea, really. He's been emailing me for weeks, possibly even months: situation dire, please come. Please send help. Please do *some*thing. Her house is full of dog-shit and flies, she isn't eating. She can't walk; she broke a hip and it didn't heal right. Her friend can't do anything for her. She won't even let him in the house anymore. She needs a relative.

I've blown him off. Blown her off. To hell with her, I said. I said it to him, just as I said it to other friends of hers who have contacted me over the years, just as I said it to myself. But lately this man's pleas have grown absolutely frantic. When the emails got nothing out of me, he started calling on the phone. My mother is now missing entirely, he tells me. Many of her belongings are on the porch. He thinks it's possible she's captive in the basement, possibly even dead down there. Still, I do nothing. I ignore these desperate phone calls almost every day for another week or more.

Then he calls again. Caring more than I did, he has contacted nursing homes and finally located her. Come now, come now, come now. So here I come. Here we come, my husband and I, to rescue Barbara.

We're going by car because we plan to try and bring her back here to Albuquerque, if she'll let us. And we know she won't fly. When she left, she took a train.

When we get to Tijeras, I laugh. Closer already, I say. We make jokes that we could have moved to Zuzax and pretend we did it to be closer to my mother. We realize we could have said the same when we moved one house down on our street: closer to my mother. We make lots of jokes about distance and time.

I haven't laid eyes on her for seventeen years.

CATCHING FISH

I caught a fish once. It was almost an accident.

When I was little, we belonged to a "nudist colony". That's in quotes because it wasn't really a nudist colony. It was just a... clubhouse sort of, with a scummy pond. If by "clubhouse" you mean a ratty little shack with a couch, and if by "couch" you mean an old truck seat with a big rip in it. It was a mile or so from our house. We'd go every week, and be naked. The few other children swam in the scummy pond but my mother wouldn't let me, really, and I didn't want to anyway. There was a raft, which I was allowed to wade out and sit on.

She only did it, I think, for the shock value of being able to tell people we were nudists. "Oh yes, we're nudists, we have no body shame, we have full membership at the Shady Lakes Nudist Colony, where I hang out with like-minded adults, and Cass can play with children her age that have no unhealthy hang-ups about their bodies."

Thing was, Shady Lakes didn't actually *require* nudity. So a lot of people there wore clothes. When my dad came (which was quite rare; I remember him there only twice in the year or so we were members), he wore bathing trunks. There were plenty of men wearing nothing, certainly, so I got to see all sorts of penises. I also got to see all sorts of old men wearing trunks. And I saw these children there, children far healthier, muscular and more tan than I. They put me in the mind of Adonis, some of them. Small versions, though, these beautiful people. Very small for gods. I came to call them (in my mind only, never out loud) the Little Gods. The little gods went fishing on the raft. And I never joined them... but one time I was on the raft first and the little gods came wading and splashing along to clamber aboard and fish. They teased me because I was not fishing, and they teased me because I did not even have a pole. They showed me their fancy official fishing poles. There were three little gods on the raft, and each one laughed at me. I was still young enough then to take that in stride and work to better myself in their eyes, so after enduring this teasing for a while, I looked around and found a piece of yarn in the pond (I told you, this pond was filthy) and then I picked up a piece of hominy corn one of the gods had let fall onto the raft from a bowl of Posole they had managed to bring with them to eat. And the little gods laughed and laughed and laughed at me for thinking I could catch a fish on a piece of red yarn, using a bit of corn. Oh, how they laughed at me... but the real gods took pity on me, for the very instant I dipped my red yarn in the water, a fish came and took the bait and I pulled it up. I held it in my hand – it was lovely, colored like a rainbow. Once the little gods had all seen it, I apologized to the fish and put it back in the water. This drew so much harsh criticism I had to leave the raft and I was never really welcome there again. Not that I was to begin with.

Shortly after this, there was a body-painting contest. All the adults were supposed to paint their children. I forget the prize, a watermelon or something. My mother did not want to get paint on herself, so she refused to paint me. The little gods were all covered from head to toe in flowers and butterflies. I was near tears with feeling left out so a woman finally came to paint on me. She warned me up front that she wasn't very good at it, and this was no word of a lie. She painted a stick figure on my belly. I did not win any prizes. The woman apologized and said it was fun anyway, wasn't it? I said yes, to be polite, but really it had not been much fun. The paint was cold and I didn't even know her. She took my picture for me, to remember it by. Not that I'd have forgotten, but how could she know?

I still have the Polaroid picture of myself on this day, naked with the hideous stick figure on my belly. In my mind, I have one also of the little gods, with their winning butterflies. In my mind, they are still jeering at me for refusing to kill the little fish.

The last time we were there, it was a 4th of July party. We hung out there the entire day just so we could see a fireworks display when the sun went down. But my mother burned her finger on a Sparkler so we had to leave before the fireworks started.

Shady Lakes ceased operating as a nudist colony a long time back, and devoted the space to farming water lilies. Hardly anyone seems to know they were ever anything other than a water lily farm. They're closed now, though, so they aren't even that.

YELLOW TEXAS

I really don't travel much. I haven't been to Texas in a long time. Longer for Oklahoma. I'd say I've never been east of there, but it's not technically true; my uncle took me to Washington D.C. once, when I was twelve or so, maybe thirteen. That's as east as it gets, I guess. But I've never been to Arkansas, or Tennessee, or the Carolinas. I've never been to Amarillo, which means *yellow* in Spanish. And it is.

Because one of my bosses has just given me a cell phone that can text, I text her when I cross the border: TEXAS. It's not a smart phone, so it takes some doing. I text her as we cross each border. She has given me the partial week off, paid, to take care of this situation. My other boss has given me the time off without pay. I work two part time jobs, making up a full-time schedule from pieces I found lying around like scraps. Even with the partly paid week, this will be a hardship. It's a gamble we're taking, that my dear mother will be able to repay us for the cost of this. My husband is doing it out of kindness; the thought of my mother rotting in a nursing home disturbs him a great deal. It doesn't disturb me much. But I *am* curious about what's going on, and my uncle is somewhat concerned. For his sake, as well as to soothe my husband and satisfy my own curiosity, I have undertaken this.

13

I am very angry with my mother. It's been four years since the last time I heard her voice. Caller ID be praised. That's how angry I am; I pretended not to be home until she finally quit trying. I let the voice mail fill up and I never emptied it, so it wouldn't accept new messages. That was a couple of years ago.

In Amarillo, we stay in a motel with an apparent herd of buffalo. All night long, they rearrange the furniture in the room above ours, and thunder up and down the hallways. I have never heard so much racket – but again, I haven't traveled much. I am worried about things, and can't sleep. We are up with the sun and I am emotionally overworked.

We breakfast in a dive on the outskirts of the city. I watch a couple berate their little boy for his every action. He does not sit up correctly, he doesn't eat his food correctly. He is a quiet boy; I cannot hear his replies. His mother harps and harps; I hear her fine. I hate her voice. I sigh.

What will my mother have to say? I wonder. And: will she agree to come with us? When she left, she vowed never to return. Never, on pain of death. That's what she said. But things change. That was then, I think. This is now.

ROSES AND ROSES
AND ROSES

My grandmother was a painter. Literally, her maiden name was Painter – we always joked this was the reason she decided to paint. She never really painted anything from her imagination. She painted copies of scenes she found on greeting cards. And then she copied *those* things over and over. Duplicates for her sorority friends. I think sometimes they had little arts & crafts fairs, and she sold her paintings for a few dollars there. The duplicates. For her sorority, she painted a yellow rose in a vase. I think that was from an actual rose a Sister gave to her for the purpose of painting, yellow roses being their official thing. Then, of course, each Sister had to have one. She copied that over and over and over. God, dozens of them.

She painted a little church scene. The Sorority wanted lots of those, too. I have the original greeting card she took it from, somewhere in a box. Along with her charm bracelet. Beta Sigma Phi gave her a charm seemingly every week for something she'd done, some internal award system they had. A star for this, a star for that, a special little heart, another, another... the bracelet is crammed so full it's hardly recognizable as a bracelet. And there are dozens of unattached charms, loose in the box. She was a star Sister. Of course those particular women are probably all dead now: even being much younger than my Nana was, they were seventy when she was ninety, and now they'd be a hundred or more. I've considered looking up the Sorority and giving them the bracelet and all the charms, framed maybe. Lookit here. Time warp for you, a Sister from beyond the grave. A Sister from before your time, before you had your own bracelet. The whole Sorority scene was strange to me. I was fascinated by it – I was told I could join, too, when I was grown, but my Nana didn't think I'd enjoy it unless I was much, much older. Possibly now (probably now, presumably now) there are women in the same Sisterhood who were young when my Nana was earning her seemingly thousands and thousands of useless little charms. Possibly, presumably, potentially, they would be charmed by the thing if I gave it to them.

Nana also made choir-singer decorations out of old phone books (so tacky!), felt Cardinals to use on your Christmas tree (so cute!), Chile Ristra plaques out of white bread dough (so clever!). She made huge felt Kachina wall-hangings before it was considered inappropriate to appropriate native culture, before they were Native and were still just Indians. Oh goodness, even just Injuns, right? My Nana was born in a simpler time, when Injuns were Injuns (and Squaws, oh Lord forgive us). And squaws didn't get to vote until my Nana was 19. So we have to give her a little slack, the poor dear. She was a good person, and she wore a Dashiki around the house back in the 70s to be cool and with-it. She'd have been mortified to discover that was wrong or that making felt Kachinas and Thunderbirds was offensive – she just thought the other cultures were adorable. And all of these things, her Sorority friends thought were adorable, too, so she made them over and over and over.

My mother liked the Thunderbirds, actually, so my Nana made one for her. We hung it in the hallway outside my bedroom door and I could see it from my bed. It scared me a little, but I liked it anyway. I liked all of the things my Nana made: the stupid choir singers, the felt birds, the endless parade of boring Church scenes. She painted two paintings the family liked, and these were original – not from a postcard, not from a greeting card, but from a thing Nana had actually seen with her eyeballs. One was a flowering Yucca. My father later requested and was given it, for which my mother never forgave either of them. It hung in his house until he died, whereupon his stupid girlfriend took it. I never saw it again. Lord knows what her kids will do with it when she dies. Probably dump it at Goodwill, where most of my father's things were reportedly taken when he died. That prunefaced woman left virtually nothing at all behind in the house that wasn't expressly left to me in his will. All of his clothes, his records, personal items, poof. Goodwill, she said. Saving you the heartbreak of going through all those things, she said.

The other painting – the *only* other painting – my Nana did that the family really appreciated was the one of the roses in a bowl. A friend brought her the roses, which were lovely, and Nana put them in a bowl on her dining room table, and she painted them. I saw the original roses. I saw the original painting, which Nana hung on the wall behind her couch. But my mother wanted it, and so did one of Nana's sisters-in-law. So Nana copied it, as was her way. She gave a copy to the sister-in-law. She gave a copy to my mother. We hung it up, but it wasn't the same and my mother never liked it quite as well. When Nana died, Uncle Bob got the original – Barbara was pissed about that, of course. She demanded that he exchange with her for the copy she had but I don't think he agreed to it. I hope he didn't, because the one my mother had was lost forever.

OK IS ALSO A PLACE

Oklahoma time. We go through it quickly. It starts off just as yellow as Texas and then it turns green, green, green. It's beautiful, but I hate it. My father's side of the family is here, the few I know about. I don't tell them I am passing through. I don't have anything in common with them. My mother and I visited here once when I was a kid – I remember the Greyhound bus trip, the sandwiches we ate in the terminal, the Count Chocula cereal my Aunt offered us for breakfast and how I wasn't allowed to have any until it was revealed that no breakfast was the other choice. I remember my Aunt and Barbara singing tunes into the night, and the guitar my aunt was playing and the Cher album they were singing along with. I was very young then; the Cher song was a 1971 hit.

Some years later, my cousin, reminiscing, said our mothers had been drinking together that day. No, I said. Absurd. My mother wasn't drinking then, I told her. I thought my cousin was just stretching, reaching, trying to have something in common, a shared experience. Driving out now, though, I wonder. Maybe she *was* drunk then, on her trip to visit Papa's family, inexplicably without him. Because over the past decade or so, I've learned a lot of things I was told as gospel truths were not true at all. Now I wonder why we were even there. It just sounds strange now, all of a sudden, that trip. I suspect her motives, her every motive.

We press on through Arkansas, and then into Tennessee.

CRIME AND PUNISHMENT

When I was probably around seven, maybe only six, I was given a drum. It was a cheap drum, and very little sound emitted from it when I tapped it with the drumsticks. I tried it harder, then harder still, and eventually managed to poke a hole in the thing. That made some sound, at last: an interesting "Pock!" Having created a hole in it, there was no reason not to do that again, so I punctured it two more times: Pock! Pock! But obviously this would not work as a musical device for long this way. I turned it over and drummed at the other side normally for a few minutes (still to no real effect – I now realize this toy drum had "skin" on both sides, which is probably why it didn't work) and then I put it in the closet. I figured I was done with it – especially as it made no noise when used in the correct fashion. But if I were to try it again, I reasoned that one really only needs one surface of the drum to be whole, anyway. I saw no reason to mention the damage. It was mine, and it should still technically work as well as it ever did.

My mother discovered the drum in there a short time later, maybe a week or two. Her rage was terrifying. She tore my room to pieces. She overturned my furniture and threw all of my toys (a meager selection, to be sure) on the floor. Then she picked up the drum along with the three toys she knew I liked best, dragged me outside and made me watch her throw them into the ditch. She made me watch them float away. She then shoved me back into my room with the demand that I "clean up this mess you caused!" and she slammed the door on me.

This incident is the reason I think perhaps my mother was not quite as sober as she claimed to be during my childhood. When the *Mommie, Dearest* movie came out many years later, I was triggered by the wire-hanger scene and I cried. I cried and cried. When I saw *Dogville*, just a few years ago, I cried and cried and cried – not when the woman was raped, not when the town was burned to the ground, not when all of the people were killed. I cried when the figurines were broken as a punishment. I cried as though someone had just taken my most precious (and as it turned out later, irreplaceable) things and thrown them into a ditch.

I cry way too much, I'm told. It's probably true. I'm crying again now, of course. Jesus. It was a little plastic nothing, the toys were all little bits of plastic nothing. But it wasn't really about that, was it? It wasn't. It wasn't at all about the toys I could not replace. It was, then and now, about how easily things can be taken from you. It was about discovering that mothers can suddenly be enraged enough to drag a screaming and terrified girl to a ditchback, there to drown her favorite things, drown them forever. To possibly throw her in as well, right? How in the world was I to know she wouldn't? She might have. She very well might have considered it many times. In retrospect, I'm almost sure of it. Throwing things away was what she did best.

ARRIVING EAST

We reach Tennessee in the dark, drive until our bones ache, check into our hotel exhausted, and experience the howl of tornado sirens immediately. I've never heard these before; they are exciting and frightening. This is so new to me, this is all so new. We herd into the hotel lobby to sit in the "safe room" until the howls abate. Several travelers are there with us. The staff finds our fright amusing; they are bored with sirens. After I've been in Tennessee for a few hours, I am, too. They never stop. We eventually just go back to our room, ignore the sirens, and go to sleep.

In the daytime, Tennessee is a long, long tunnel of kudzu vines. Trees grow like huge walls around us on both sides of the road and the vines smother them; there is no horizon. There is precious little sky. I have never seen the like of it. We drive forever, and eventually burst out the end into North Carolina. It is beautiful. I hate it already.

CANARIES

Canaries changed my life. I remember the day I came home from school and she had the first canary. He was orange, and I named him Carrot. She, as always, escalated things rapidly, and by the time her marriage ended she had an entire aviary full of canaries and canary things to get rid of. Also lovebirds, also parrots, also cockatiels, also lorikeets. We were bird people, then, like we had once been horse people, like we had once been mouse people. I was in the fourth grade when she got the canaries, and within a few months she had a full-on breeding program. Since I had named her first canary, she asked me to name her canary-breeding business. I named it Birdsong Aviary and she had business cards printed. I was so proud. (She later had a small fight with a local bookstore by the name of Birdsong Books.)

My mother, having so much going on with the bird business, wanted help around the house. We'd had a woman named Armenia helping out once a week, but she had gone back to Mexico – this was when we found out she was here illegally; my parents actually had to smuggle her back *into* Juarez and help her get to her family. Anyway, my mother wanted help with the housework, so my dad moved a singlewide trailer onto our pastureland, and we had one of his friends' daughters move in, the idea being that she could pay a little bit of cash rent money and then help out around the house to make up the rest. Her name was Janice and she was overweight and had an unfortunate piggy nose. Janice was a lazy slob and she did nothing at all to help, and did not pay anything either, so they kicked her out after only a few months.

One of my mother's bird-breeding friends suggested this man she knew who needed a place to stay. He was a nice guy, she said, down on his luck and pretty broke. He had lots of problems. And that was Bernard, who must have arrived during the fall when I was in the 5th grade.

I liked him. Bernard was in his early thirties and had long hair, a goofy smile, big blue eyes and a bad back. He was driving a school bus part time and refinishing furniture to make ends meet. He had, we were told, been taught to cane chairs as part of his rehabilitation – because caning chairs is a thing you can do even if you are in a wheelchair, which Bernard was expected to be. His business cards named him as *The Chair Doctor*.

So, out with Janice, in with Bernard. My parents sold him our old VW bus so he could transport furniture more easily. Bernard was a lot of fun. He was like a kid. Bernard loved kids. He played with me, gave me junk food, acted silly, took me to movies. He planted a garden and let me help; he planted an entire row of sunflowers just because I said I loved them. He introduced me to his across-town uncle Lorenzo, and I became fast friends with Lorenzo's daughter right away. Bernard taught me to call him Bernie. When Bernard went to visit his mother in Colorado, he brought back toys for me. I adored Bernard, so it was not really hard for my mother to get me to say yes when she asked if we should run away with him.

And then presto, we did. My father moved to an apartment for a time and my mother had Bernard sleeping with her in their bed, which was a secret. She would sneak him in via the side door, after I was in bed.

In the 6th grade, my English teacher had us reading horror stories in the dark, with a flashlight. It was October; for a whole week or maybe two weeks, we read Tales of the Midnight Hour. I had night terrors and could not sleep, so I ran to my mother's room. The door was locked. That was horrifying, too. It had never been locked. I pounded and screamed, sure I was about to be carved to bits by a man with a machete. She kept – unfathomably – saying no. No, go to bed. No no no, you can't come in. I persisted, totally hysterical. Probably a psychologist would have things to say about all this. I knew it wasn't rational, but I could not contain my terror. I kept wailing and pounding at the door with increasing fervor. There was a crash and a scream... and then Bernard answered the door, naked. My mother had tripped on a table they had been refinishing, which they had taken the top off of and brought inside so it would dry more evenly. She had finally been coming to open the door and calm me down, but then, having clearly broken a toe, had sent Bernard in her stead. Naked Bernard did take my mind off the machete killer, at least. But this is how I remember when Bernard started sleeping in my mother's bed: marked in time by Mr. Baldwin and his Tales, cemented firmly by my mother's broken toe and Bernard's erect penis.

The next day my mother told me it was a secret-secret-secret that she had slept with Bernard before the divorce was final, because if my father knew he would win everything in the divorce and he would kill Bernard. Kill him with a gun or beat him to death. I had nightmares about that for months, too. It was rough on me: Bernard with his huge scars all over his body from back surgeries, stomach surgeries, kind little Bernard like a brother to me, so frail... imagining my father, a full-grown man, attacking him. I was horrified. Of course I would never breathe a word of it and I would never *ever* tell him we planned to move away with Bernard once the divorce was final. Because, remember, Cass, this divorce was all your idea. You wanted me to leave your father and run away with Bernard. You're the one making me do this, so you have to be very quiet or it can't happen.

After we lived with Bernard for a couple of years, he convinced my mother there was really no such thing as alcoholism and she could drink wine if she wanted to.

And that's how the canaries changed my life.

When I spoke to Bernard a few years ago, he said he had no idea my mother left my father to be with him. He thought it had just been a coincidence. I don't know if I believe that.

IN ASHEVILLE

We have arranged for a hotel very near my mother's house, walking distance to French Broad street. But we don't walk, because we are unfamiliar and tired. We check in, then drive past her house, just for reference, to place it in our minds and see it with our eyes. The gate is shut. A dog stares at us. I imagine what I will find inside there. I imagine a lot of things, some of them not good. I've been given a mental picture of the breakdown that had been long going on inside these walls. My mother, I think, will be essentially herself. But her house? I can't know. There is, as I was warned, a great pile of items on her porch. I cannot see what they are.

There is a sign out front that says "by appointment only." What the hell does that mean?

We return to our hotel and map out our plan. My uncle, Barbara's brother, has provided us with a Power of Attorney that should enable us to start taking over her life and get her sorted out. We need to get her to sign it. Then we need to visit the man living in her house, or at least post a notice of intent to enter. We have to find out what's actually going on here. It's not as if we know. I tried some weeks ago to involve her estranged husband, but he wasn't interested. When he left, he did not intend to come back. It's a familiar theme; all footprints seem to lead away from this lion's den, and none return. But I have to. For whatever reason, I have to go back in.

STAYIN' ALIVE

Big hit song in the year my parents separated. Another was (Your Love Has Lifted Me) Higher and Higher by Rita Coolidge. My mother turned up the radio every time that one came on. She said that was *their* song: hers and Bernie's. She sang along. His love had lifted her higher. Than she'd ever. I was happy for her.

We spent a couple of weeks looking for a house that would be close to my father. Walking distance, my mother said. This was extremely limiting, under the circumstances. The first house we considered seriously had only one bedroom. This house was very close indeed; about a quarter of a mile away. It was actually an antique store we had visited several times, run by a woman named Cici and her husband (whose name I forget). They were closing the store and selling the building; the idea was Bernard and my mother could sleep in the only bedroom, and they would put a couch in the antique store for me to sleep on. As to my things, books, toys, that stuff... well, I would just walk to my father's house to play with those. And I could keep one or two books at the new place.

Being a good-natured kid, I was fine with this idea. Fortunately, Bernard had more sense than this and he told us both that wasn't realistic at all, that a kid needs a room. So, we ended up in a tiny, tiny place about a mile away from my father's house. And even though it was within walking distance, I was never allowed to try it, because the street was so dangerous and there was no sidewalk. This new house had a room for me that was six feet wide by ten feet long, much less space than I had before. There was no door on the room, so we hung a red bead curtain in the doorway. There was no closet. I was told that my old room would still be mine, so I could keep most of my stuff there. But when my father moved back home, he brought with him a woman he had met at the apartments. And she wanted all those toys gone, for the room was to become a guest room. Still your room, Cassie, of course. But just without any of your *things*. So, if you want these things, you better come get them, my father said. He had no idea how small my new room was, and didn't care much under the circumstances. So, when I failed to take the toys and books, he got rid of them to please Pam. Shortly thereafter, also to please Pam, he painted over all the paintings my mother had done on the walls: flowers and birds. She had copied them largely from my childhood book of fairy tales, which was one of the ones that had been given away when I didn't find room for it. If I'd known he was going to paint over the birds, I may have tried harder to keep that book. I loved those paintings.

A couple of years ago I searched online and found a copy of that old book, and bought it. I spent hours staring at the birds. The book seems much smaller than it was then. So do the birds. I love them anyway. I love them – but I cry every time I look at them.

OBSTREPEROUS BARBARA

Following the directions we've been given, we locate the nursing home my mother has been ensconced in, sign the register, find the elevator. It's very like a hospital, I think. My husband sends me in alone; he pretends it's out of respect for our relationship, but I know it's simple fear. Dread.

The woman who approaches me bears little resemblance to my mother. She's a foot shorter than she should be, for one thing; shorter than I am, where my mother was always considerably taller. This hag is utterly toothless. She is leaning on a walker, making slow progress. I cannot be sure it is her; these rooms are semi-private. This could be someone else's mother, someone else's problem. I worry, because it's been so long, that maybe I really won't know her. When she reaches me, though, she says, "Are you here to help me get to the bathroom? I promise not to be too obstreperous." Then there is no doubt. Who else would say such a thing? It's her. She proves it again immediately by demanding I come into the bathroom with her to wipe her ass, and becoming petulant and childish when I tell her she can do that herself. Classic Barbara. My laughter and shouts of annoyance draw my husband, and I tell him we have found her.

She does not recognize me, though. That takes longer.

CASS IS DOING FINE

So we left a big house to move into a small house. It wasn't so much that I went from hoping my father would make burgers for dinner or hoping for my mother's famous pork chops to our being unable to afford meat at all. It wasn't just that I had no toys and there was a woman rearranging furniture in my old room, badmouthing my mother, painting over my beloved birds, sticking a fork in my little hand if I reached for anything at the dinner table when I was visiting instead of asking for it to be passed – something I had never once, ever, been required to do. Nor was it my father shrugging when I burst into tears at this ridiculous woman *forking* me when I reached for the butter, smugly forking me and smirking. "You need to learn your manners, little missy." My father just kept eating. Probably true, he likely was thinking. Barbara didn't teach this kid any manners at all. But the butter was right in front of me. She had to reach *over* the butter to stab me, that bitch. And she dragged me, literally *dragged* me, across grocery store picket lines, which was anathema to me. Her politics were repulsive. My father later admitted he had located the first woman who was the most unlike my mother he could find, and that was the primary reason why he was with her. He hadn't had far to go to find her – she was in the apartment complex he stayed in during the separation. Her apartment was the mirror image of his, directly across the courtyard. I mean, it's possible he found her the day he moved there. It seemed that way, to me, then. Now I think she found *him*.

It wasn't any one of these things in particular, just that it was a lot of changes at once. A great lot of changes. But I was handling it. I was described as doing just *fine*. Cass has no problems at all. Happy as she can be, that girl; she wanted this, this is just what she wanted. Cass requested all of this. And really, I *was* pretty happy. Bernard was a lot of fun, after all. And my mother seemed happy, which made me happy. And then, a few weeks after we moved into the tiny house where my mother and Bernard shared a bed openly, Bernard got very sick. He was in the hospital for a while. For a long while, actually. I was sent to live with my grandmother for about a month when I was in the seventh grade. They removed almost all of his intestines. They sent him home again briefly, but he developed a huge abscess and was back in the hospital again. And that time when he came back, he had to have a nurse come every day to change his dressing. And we had to put out a rollaway bed and pretend that was his bed, because he wasn't allowed to be living with us as my mother's boyfriend. In order to keep getting his benefits, he had to be a *boarder*. And I had to treat him as though I hardly even knew him, even though I'd seen him naked a hundred times and had run my fingers all over the scars on his back and these new ones on his belly. Even though my mother had left my father for him, even though for weeks or months my mother had insisted I should call Bernard my "father" (to his credit, Bernard insisted that was not right and I should absolutely not do this), and even though I had stayed in the care of my grandmother for a month or more, deeply worried that he would actually *die,* I now had to act, when the nurse was there, when the social workers were there, like he was just some guy. He was just the new Janice. Helps out around the house. Look, he canes chairs.

And then they went back to college together, and I became a latchkey kid. While my mother studied mental illnesses and Bernard worked toward his dream of being a schoolteacher, that's where almost every penny went: for their classes and books. And when they both finally had finished school and gotten jobs that paid a little better, they rearranged the house a little to improve our lives. And that's when it all fell apart.

BEING RECOGNIZED

After the bathroom, I follow my mother back to her bed. She talks about how this place isn't much fun. She holds her cards close to her vest; I cannot tell quite what she is thinking. I ask how she got here. She says her friend put her in here but that she will go back home soon. I ask if this friend of hers visits. She says not often, not for a long while. I ask if anyone else visits her, and she says her other friend sometimes does, and that he and the nurses told her that her daughter would visit soon but she knows that's not true.

"I'm your daughter," I say. "I *am* here to visit you." The wreck in the bed looks at me, furious. She accuses me of having sport with her. I can't shake the feeling that it's the other way around, that this is an act she's putting on. I tell her, again, I am her daughter. I am Cass. "Look at me, Mom. It's me. Can't you tell it's me?"

She looks at me long, long. "Cass? *Cassie?* Is that you? It IS you!" And then: "Oh my God. Cassie...you got *old*."

Indeed, I did.

JUST CASS

My mother dressed me in boys clothes, because she didn't want people to assume I was a girl. She cut my hair short – not even a neat and tidy short, but a choppy razor blade job, uneven, all directions. She said it made me look like Mia Farrow. Which it did, a little. If I wore a cute little sundress, which was a rarity. In my boy's jeans and white t-shirts I looked like an orphaned starveling. Please sir, may I have some more?

My mother almost never permitted anyone to call me Cassie. My grandmother called me Cassie now and then, and my mother always railed at her. Cass, she said. Not Cassie. That was atrocious. Too cutsie. Too *girly*. My mother only called me Cassie when she was being silly or admonishing me. And later, when she was drunk.

I'm a bit preoccupied with the subject of *names*. My mother told me she named me *Cass* so that nobody would know whether I was a boy or a girl just from my name. She said she didn't want anyone to make judgments about me, thinking I was female just automatically. *Cass*, she said, could be either a man or a woman. Like *Jesse*, which was the other name she said she had considered before deciding on *Cass* because it was more unique. She said she would have named me *Cass* regardless of my gender. Thank heavens I turned out female. I drew enough scathing remarks from classmates as it was; I can't imagine the beatings I'd have suffered as a boy with this name.

She didn't give me a middle name, which was another source of irritation. Every school form, middle initial... blank. Cass, dear, you need to put down your middle initial. What is your middle name? What do you mean you don't have a middle name? Worse: Cass, NA is two letters. You can only put one in. What does NA stand for? What do you mean 'not applicable'? My mother told me I could choose my own middle name when I was older. In the meantime, she said, I could just try on any names I liked and see how I felt about them. She hated her own middle name, which was June. She had been born in June. If she'd been born in May, she would have been Mary Margaret. (Nana told me that if my uncle, born at Christmastime, had been a girl, he'd have been Holly Jessica. I wonder if he knows that. Probably he does). June made my mother Barbara June, and she hated her mother for that despised name. I think my mother would have disliked Mary Margaret equally, though she insisted not. But for those reasons and more, she wanted to give me an unusual name. Cass. No, not short for Cassandra. Not short for Cassiopeia. Cassie maybe? No. Not short for... anything. Just Cass. Try to make someone get that on the phone, ever once. Cathy did you say? Cath? Cash? Was that Tess? Did you say Kathy? Is that with a K? Kath? Add in the last name and it gets funnier. Cosmic Main? Jasmine May? What... oh – Cass! I see ...you were named after Mama Cass? No? You know she choked to death on a sandwich, don't you, yuk yuk yuk... (she didn't). Cass, Cass... is that short for Cassandra? Oh Jesus, how many times. Eventually I started telling people it was short for Casserole. You know, Cass. Like a casserole? My mother just wanted to signify her love of good tuna casserole. Her favorite casserole dish broke the day I was born, she thought it was a sign. Later I told people it was short for Casket. I was conceived in a... well, you get the idea.

How could I be so mean, my mother asked, to lie to people about my perfectly acceptable name that would never lead anyone to pre-judgement based on my sex? How could I grow so annoyed with those who assumed it must be short for something? I had a story to tell! I had this fabulous name that nobody else had, I was unique! Yeah. But kids don't want to be unique, do they? Kids want to fit in. I wanted to be named Lisa or Emily or Anna. I wanted to have an equally insignificant middle name, a *saint's* name like all the girls around me in our predominantly Catholic area had. I wanted to be Mary Margaret.

In the second grade, filling out papers for a new school, I took my mother at her word and tried on a name I liked. I filled in my middle initial as J, and I told the teacher my middle name was Julie. The teacher called my mother to make sure of my records. Appalled, my mother told her no, I had no middle name and certainly if I had one it would not be *Julie*. In the third grade, I tried again: Melody. (That was one of my Nana's faves). My mother gave me a speech about not pulling this again, that I could pretend all I wanted to but I must stop filling in fake initials on official documents. I could have a middle name when I was old enough to choose one myself. No, I could not choose now because I had proven I would choose something abhorrent like Julie or Melody. When I was sixteen, she said.

And when I was sixteen, I did. I chose *Jesse*, for the name I always wished she had chosen instead of Cass. I did spend about six weeks trying to get people to call me CJ that year, but it was too late. I was Cass forever by then.

VIEW OF THE ROOFTOP

She says she is hungry, so we walk to the lunchroom. She sits at a huge banquet table, demands cookies, makes a mess with them. She asks for coffee. A young man brings her coffee and she looks at him as though he's lost his mind. It is, she says imperiously, far too hot for coffee. What can he be thinking? Coffee at lunchtime, ridiculous. But lunch was served hours ago, she's already been fed, they tell me. She simply won't eat anything but cookies. Miz Barbara has a sweet tooth, the nurse says. Yes, I imagine she does. I follow her back down the hall. She goes to the hall window and tells me the view will be of a rooftop. It is. Inside her room again, she says it's a shame I am only in town for a short while, because she may be in the hospital for a few more weeks and she wanted me to see her house. Then she tells me she has Robert DeNiro tied up in her basement as a sex slave, and says with relish, "No matter how old you are, you still get horny!"

The second time I walk her down the hallway, she sees a laundry hamper and asks what it is. The nurse there tells her. "She asks what it is every time she sees it," she adds for my benefit. "Don't you, Miz Barbara?" We shuffle along. The nurse gives me a dirty look; Barbara's pants are wet. I shrug. If they want her pants dry, they can dry her. When I asked

40

her if she shouldn't use a new pair of incontinence pants, she acted like I was nuts. She only has one, she says. I think she may be mistaken, but there are in fact none in the room, so I can't be sure.

Her anxiety is through the roof. "Where am I, Cassie? What am I doing? Where are we going?" I explain again and again where she is, and who put her there. "This place is pretty nice, really," she says. "If it weren't a hospital." A few moments later she hisses, "I *despise* it here."

When we reach the end of the hall, she again tells me the view will be of a rooftop. And, again: it is.

HOW IT FELL APART

How it fell apart was this: They insulated the tiny attic and converted it to a bedroom. That freed up her former bedroom, see, which had been partitioned off from the living room with old barnwood. Could I have that larger bedroom now? No, I could not. The plan was to remove the tacky barnwood partition and reinstate the room as a dining room. So we could have class. My mother was big on class. She bought classical records by the dozen. An antique dining room table was procured – very similar to the one that broke her toe, she pointed out. And then we bought china from Sears. Fine china and fine glassware. And once we had glassware, we had to have wine glasses. She had this clear vision: fine music, fine art, fine glassware. And if you have wine glasses, you need wine to drink from them. She bought alcohol-free wine, and sipped it daintily from the fine glassware. That lasted a few months. But she got drunk on this non-alcoholic wine, so she said. Bernard said that was proof she wasn't an alcoholic at all. It was all in her head. He told her that more than once.

She started openly drinking real wine when I was seventeen. When I saw her doing that, I walked up and tried to take a sip from her glass. She wouldn't let me. She claimed that she had never once told me I could drink from her glass. She told me that alcoholism stuff was never really a thing. She denied ever having had any sort of drinking problem. And she kept it under control, for a while. She got another promotion, and when I graduated from high school we moved to a bigger house downtown. Then I had a bedroom upstairs, too.

FRED'S SHOES

When we visit again later in the day, the nurses have washed Barbara, changed her pants. Her hair is combed, smooth and clean. "Doesn't she look nice?" they say, and my mother looks at me and asks the same. Yes, she looks nice, I say. Better, anyway. I pet her hair. It's so soft. It always was soft, softer and finer than my own.

In the hallway, some commotion. A man in a wheelchair is rolling slowly down the hall, asking loudly about the whereabouts of his shoes. "Where are my shoes?" he cries at everyone he passes. "I need my shoes. Someone took 'em!" A nurse takes his chair by the handles and turns him around, wheels him back the way he came. "But my shoes!" he says. "I need my shoes!"

The nurse shakes her head. "On your feet, Fred." I think she means he needs to get out of the chair until she adds, "Your shoes. They're on your feet, Fred. Look down." She keeps pushing him back to his room over his protests, saying again and again in reply to his demands, "Your shoes are on your feet, Fred. You have them on your feet. On your feet." She sees me watching and rolls her eyes tiredly. He does this all the time, she says. She says that with the air of one who has not only to deal with Fred and his shoes several times a day but also with people like me, spectators. She says it with the air of one who knows hell is other people. "They're always on his feet," she says. "Aren't they, Fred? That's right."

As she passes by, another man catches my eye, sitting in a chair in the hallway. He's waving at me, beckoning at me to come nearer. I do. He gazes at my face, beaming. "Your visit," he says quite earnestly. "It means so much to me. It's the whole world."

I nod and smile. Who does he think I am? A daughter maybe? A sibling? Lover? Some old friend? I don't want to add to the darkness in his life, so I just nod and smile. "I'm glad to hear that," I tell him.

He continues to gaze at me lovingly. "I mean it, every word," he says as I turn to go. "Your visit means the absolute world to me. Please come back soon." I promise I will. I promise that easily because I think it will ease his mind and I doubt it will matter: surely he tells all the visitors the same thing, just as Fred laments his lost shoes, and my mother puzzles over the laundry hamper; day in and day out, it's always the same day around here. Because hell is other people and we don't always die off neatly like we should. Sometimes we linger, zombielike.

I leave the man behind, still calling after me that my visit means the absolute world to him. I go back across the hall to my mother and her damn soft hair. My mother, for whom my visit means almost literally nothing. I wonder how long she will linger.

MY UPSTAIRS BEDROOM

In my upstairs bedroom, I was well-placed to watch my mother grow increasingly nuts. Her drinking went up, up, up. She played with her gun all the time. With her loaded gun. Right under me, where I lay in my bed, my mother threatened to shoot herself, to shoot Bernard, to shoot the fucking *dog*. She had a new job, working with mental patients at the jail, and she fell hard for one of the mental inmates. He played guitar, so she obtained a tape of him singing. She played it all the time. And I mean, really, all the time. She kept me awake, playing it at midnight, one, two in the morning. If I complained, she turned it up higher. Screamed at me. Listen to him, listen, listen, he's *beautiful*.

She told me he was her real son.

She hatched a plan to help him escape from the jail. She asked me if I thought our basement was livable enough to hide a grown man in for a few weeks or months.

Seriously, she asked me that. If I had said yes, she probably planned to say it had been my own idea.

We lived with Bernard until I turned eighteen. I moved away the following spring. Bernard moved away a few weeks later. I consider him lucky: one of the escapees. He told me he had stayed until I was gone, to protect me, but that once I left, it got worse. He said she threatened to shoot him every day, and he asked me never to tell her where he went, because he was afraid she'd hunt him down.

She was too lazy for that sort of thing; I don't think she ever tried to find him. But she did try in earnest to convince me to complain that he had molested me, so he would lose his teaching job. I didn't do that, of course.

For a little while after Bernard left, my mother hung around in bars and took strange men home with her. One of them was a weirdo barely older than I was – and that kid was among the nicer of the weirdos she brought home. Another one stole her checkbook and forged her name on several hundreds of dollars worth of checks. The bank absorbed that mistake, because the signatures didn't bear even a slight resemblance to hers.

Shortly after that happened, Bernard's uncle Lorenzo left his wife and moved in with my mother. And then the very bad situation went totally off the rails. Because Lorenzo was the King of Enablers, and enablement was the word of the day.

I was told that Lorenzo had left his wife because she was an abusive out-of-control drunk who had come after him with a hatchet. He proposed to my mother the moment his divorce was final. I talked to his daughter – we both agreed this marriage was a terrible idea. We tried, both of us, to talk him out of it. But I said to my friend, well... my mother drinks, yeah. But at least she isn't going to come after him with a *hatchet* or anything. She's not *completely* out of control, I said. I thought it was true. It *was* true, at that time.

A short time – maybe a year or so, maybe less than a year – after the marriage, my mother's boss tried to change her schedule to all nights. She refused to take the graveyard shift. She told them she was married now, and had to be home at night to make dinner and keep house, that her hubby wouldn't appreciate being abandoned every night. But I suspected the main reason was it would interfere with her drinking schedule. I knew her boss and coworkers worried about her drinking; they had told me as much. She alarmed them. I thought perhaps they were changing her schedule especially to shake her up – if she worked all night, then when would she drink? And indeed, she knew it would be a problem. So she quit.

Later, I suspected the truth could have been that they had fired her for being drunk on the job. But I never did find out.

WHAT SHE'S DONE

Once we are identified as Her People, the management wants a word. Her account is in arrears. They've been getting nowhere with her friend, who does not return their phone calls. He dropped her off here some months ago, they tell us, with no identification. He's only paid a small portion of the bills. All smiles, they are, shaking their heads at our plight. Dreadful situation, but what can we do, really, you understand. Our hands are tied, surely you must understand. You must understand how it is. We're told we need to pay somewhere in the neighborhood of nine grand, please, as soon as possible. It will be twelve in another month, and they can't allow her to remain in this fine establishment indefinitely without payment. Smiles upon smiles upon smiles. We have no idea whether she has any money or not, but assure the staff members that we will look into the situation once we know what's going on.

They help us get her to sign the new Power of Attorney and have it notarized. They have a contact who understands the peculiar and specific issues faced by those needing notarized signatures from demented patients. And my mother is as demented as they come. The bill for this place comes to just over four grand a month – it's assisted living, they explain. Medicare doesn't pay for this. But they tell us that we might have luck getting her into a full care ward, which it's pretty clear she does require, and getting hooked up with Medicaid coverage, which would pay for that. We agree we must look into it, but it won't help her here: though we shouldn't have any trouble getting doctors to sign off on her need for full care, this establishment does not accept Medicaid patients. The whole conversation is confusing to me; I keep mixing the two programs up in my head. My husband tells me to think of it this way: Medicare *cares*, and they care a little bit about everyone. But Medicaid is more serious. Only a few people get aid – and if you really need aid, you have to ask for it.

We need help filing our forms, so we find an attorney within walking distance of our hotel and explain our story. The Power of Attorney forms my uncle has given us are not complete for North Carolina – we need an additional one that we don't have. He gives us the second form, and helps correct an issue with the first one, at no charge because of our plight. We, and our plight, will be leaning heavily on the kind people of Asheville, NC over the next several days. Again and again, I wish my mother had never come here.

We file our forms with the state registrar and start digging into everything. The Barbara Situation is complicated in some ways. But in another way, it's very simple: She simply gave everything she owned to a con man she found charming, because that's the kind of thing she always did when she was drunk. And my mother hadn't been anything but drunk in a long, long time.

OH, SYLVIA

When Lorenzo moved in with my mother, he brought with him a box of things that had belonged to his son. Well, actually, these things had belonged to his son's disturbed friend, who had died while in prison. How his things came to be a thing Lorenzo had to deal with, I will never know. But he brought them, and he and my mother stored them in a small closet in the upstairs hall. The disturbed friend had killed his parents. Oddly enough, my mother had worked with the boy after his arrest. It was her job, after all.

But once these things were brought, she claimed they had an evil spirit in them. And she began blaming all her problems, her own erratic behaviors, on this spirit, whom she called 'Sylvia'. The family joked about it – there were spirits involved alright, we said, but not that kind. It was the drinking, we said. Did she not remember that she could not drink? But she would have none of it, of course. She said she never once had ever, ever had any sort of drinking problem.

My mother tried to stab me once, claiming it was actually Sylvia who held the knife. That happened on Thanksgiving. I had cooked the turkey that year – my first time doing it. (I'd inherited this duty because the year before, Nana failed to turn the oven on, and Thanksgiving dinner had been served around 9 pm).

THE BARBARA SITUATION

We go to her house and post a Notice of Intent to Enter on the door. Then we go to the bank; unsurprisingly, almost all of her money has been liquidated by this so-called friend of hers. We have his access to the accounts taken away. The bank manager is horrified by our story; he swears he will call the police if he sees the man again. I tell him not to waste his time – it wouldn't do any good; this is not that kind of fraud. Then we go to the Social Security office to see what we can do about applying for more help, since she has no money to pay her bills with.

Paul drops me off at the Social Security office and goes back to the hotel to start working on other phone calls that need to be made. I wait patiently for my turn. When I start explaining the story, the woman I am speaking with picks up her phone and dials an extension. She asks the person on the other end if she remembers the man who was applying for benefits on behalf of my mother a few weeks previous. "Her daughter is here, and apparently he put her in a nursing home and took all her money."

From across the room, a shout: "I knew it!" A blonde head pops up from a cubicle on the other side of the room and the woman strides in our direction, hollering triumphantly. "I knew he was no good, I knew it, I *knew* it. Didn't I *tell* you something was wrong with that guy?"

He had aroused suspicion because of what he was asking for and the weirdly elusive way he was asking for it. He came off really creepy, she said. And the woman he was with stole her pen. "I mean, it was a nice pen. She kept talking about how nice it was, and then she just stole it. Who does that?"

I explain the rest of the Barbara Situation: he left her in a nursing home with no ID, and we've just found her there. She owes them for two months already, and it will be three in a week. And she has no money, because he took it all, virtually every dime.

It's complicated, the SS people explain, as they fill out forms. In order to qualify for benefits, one must be broke in a natural way. She could keep her house, if we say she intends to live there again. I tell the women I doubt she will ever be able to return to the house, but that she certainly did say she intended to. They check that box. "Just in case," they tell me. "Maybe she will." But there must be virtually no money or assets of any other kind – and she can't have just given them away freely. We will have to demonstrate that she was taken advantage of. It will take some time. These forms alone take another hour; these women are the nicest people I have ever met in a government office in my life.

If we can demonstrate that she's been taken advantage of, we can get her on Medicaid. But that's not the whole problem. That's nowhere near the whole problem.

ASPIRIN

There was a popular inhalant sold over the counter, back in the day. The instructions on the bottle at that time were an exact account of how to use it, phrased as a warning never to use it in that manner. "Do not place one inch from your nostrils and inhale deeply," or words to that effect. I remember thinking that was hysterical when I read it. Of course, I thought the entire world was hysterical at that moment, for obvious reasons.

When I was very young, my mother reached up and fiddled with a basket on the top shelf of the tallest bookcase in the house. She did it right in front of me, eyeballing me. When I looked at her, she told me what was in the basket was something I must never, ever look at. Ever. Over the years, I caught her fiddling with that basket often, and every time I did, she would get what I now recognize as a feigned look of surprise on her face. She would act contrite; sorry, sorry, I should not get this out when you are watching. It's a bad idea, you must never be curious about this basket and its contents. Not for you, this basket. Never ever should you climb on a chair and see what is in there. Do not place one inch from your nostrils. Do not inhale deeply.

Naturally, I eventually did. What was in the basket was a

news article about a woman who tried to kill herself in April of 1966. An overdose of sleeping pills, she took.

I was born in September of 1966.

I'm told she tried this overdose trick no fewer than three times while she was pregnant with me. I'm pretty sure she wasn't trying to actually kill *herself*, you know. I was born a month premature – probably figured I better get the hell out before it was too late. I always *have* been stubborn.

When her efforts to miscarry me failed, she tried to be rid of me in other ways. Nobody has told me this. I have *intuited* it, as they say. I have found the truth by reading between the lines. There are so many lines. But the truth is so obvious now. I guess it was obvious always. My grandmother always told me I was so *thin* as a baby, she didn't think I was getting any food. Such a sickly child, so weak. She told me, with a laugh, haha, such a little thing to mention, that she kept finding me in my crib with a bottle of bourbon. And everyone in the family told me that I was special, or that I turned out amazingly well... considering. Your mother loved you, Cassie, but she was not well. Between the lines: she knew she was *supposed* to love me. She said she did, sometimes. Other times she told me she loved me, of course, because she was my mother and she had to, but that she wished I'd never been born. She told me often that I had ruined her life.

I get reminded of this every time I have to fill out forms at the doctor's office. Because whenever I visit a new doctor, I have to tell them I am allergic to aspirin. They almost always say "Aspirin, ok ...and what happens when you take aspirin?"

Well. Who knows, right? Because here's the thing: I don't think I *am* allergic to aspirin. My mother told me I was, she told me that for years and years. She told me when she gave me aspirin, I ended up in the hospital.

But I ended up in the hospital an awful lot as a child... as an *infant*, I should say. And that was when she gave me the aspirin. And when you listen to the whole story – when I did, that is, when I listened to it, over and over and over in my childhood – well, I started to read between the lines.

She told me I was sick and she gave me aspirin to bring down my fever. She said the doctor told her to do that. Maybe that's true. But then she said the doctor told her to "just give her aspirin until the fever goes down" and she admitted what she actually did was poke many, many aspirins down my throat all night long until I almost died and they had to rush me to the hospital – where she told them she had given me *an* aspirin on doctors' orders. She did not tell them she had given me at least ten aspirins, maybe more. She did not tell them she had been drinking. She didn't tell them she really never wanted a baby, or that I was stubborn and screaming and she hated me and everything I had done to ruin her life. She told them she had given me only the recommended dose of aspirin, and so they told her I must be allergic to aspirin... and that was what I had to tell every single authority I've crossed paths with since. If I have a single aspirin, I tell them, I will die.

I was just a year old when I was in the hospital for the mystery aspirin reaction. I was in and out of the hospital before and after that, one thing or another. Kidney infections, ear infections, vomiting. I remember some of it quite distinctly, actually. I remember being too young to speak in real words, and being frustrated when they gave me Jell-o with no spoon. (They obviously expected me to eat it with my fingers, but I wanted a spoon. I kept trying to ask for one but I didn't know how.) My mother told me, based on my description of the room I was in, that this had to be when I had just turned two. This hospital, she said, was the one where they allowed my IV to go dry and I got a bad infection. I ended up with a huge purple scar on my foot for years; I remember my mother explaining it to me when I was around four, telling me that I had almost died. Again. Like the other times. Well, Cassie, you were just so *sickly* all the time, we never knew what was going on.

My father issued an ultimatum when I was two. He told her he was going to leave her if she didn't sober up. And between the lines I see this: my father threatened to leave, but he didn't plan to take me with him. Girls belong with their mothers, he'd have said. Even mothers that aren't well. But fortunately I didn't have to run that gauntlet; she quit drinking. And she was loudly, famously sober for a long while.

Until she wasn't.

SOMEBODY THAT
I USED TO KNOW

We go to the police and explain our problem, ask them to look into the status of her vehicles. These have all been put into Derrick's name. We tell them the whole story, and file a complaint, just to get it on record. The police are sorry, and they sympathize, but they can't do much. They recommend urgently that we immediately issue an eviction notice. We have one already prepared, we tell them.

When the 24 hours are up, we arrive for the inspection. We hired an ex-Marine to bring with us, as backup. Derrick meets us at the gate and says he's called the police. I tell him good, I called them as well. I open the gate and Derrick blocks it with his body. He tells me I am not invited in. I tell him I don't need his invite; it's my mother's house. I fully intend to keep right on walking into the house, try-and-stop-me style, but my husband and the Marine make me wait. The police arrive; they already know the story, but pull me aside to again tell me we need to start eviction right away and be sure to do everything exactly right so this guy won't have a leg to stand on in court. Then they tell the man I have every right to enter the house and inspect it. Our Marine talks to the cop, and they both stand behind me as I walk through the gate into the house. The dogs growl at us the entire time. I am not afraid of dogs in the least. I just dare them to bite me, even slightly. One tooth. They seemingly know better, but follow us through the house, growling.

I've never been here before. My husband takes pictures, so we have a baseline. I scan the place quickly. I see things I recognize, of course, but very few of the cherished ones. I am careful to appear nonchalant when I catch sight of any item that holds meaning for me – and there is almost nothing here that doesn't mean something – because I don't want this man to have any idea what I value most out of the items he holds captive. The real treasures are all gone, anyway. There is a hospital bed in what could be the dining room. Derrick's girlfriend asks with faked concern how my mother is. I tell her Barbara has no clothes, so she opens a drawer and picks out a few things for us to take her. She also gives me a case of adult diapers. They did send her there with clothes, she tells me. They are lost, I reply.

On our way out, I mention that I assume he's taken all of her jewelry. His girlfriend runs into the house and brings me a rubber glove with a turquoise ring and a bracelet in it. She swears it's the only jewelry Barbara owned, the only jewelry they ever saw my mother wear. He says she was wearing those items when he took her to the home but they asked him to take them so they wouldn't be stolen. He tells me my mother showed him some of my writing once and he thought it was cute. I raise an eyebrow. He talks about my mother's chronic diarrhea, then turns and wipes his hands on my husband, up and down, to demonstrate the way my mother used to wipe her beshitted hands on him, to explain why he finally had to move her to a home. I am not sure which thing makes me feel more violated: that he's seen my writing (and found it cute) or that he feels free to wipe pretend shit on us. My husband does not react. Probably it was expected that he would, that this offense would inspire one of us to lash out physically. This guy is a practiced con-man.

We hand him the notice of eviction. He smirks at me and says he holds a legal lease on the house, and even though I hold the new power of attorney, I have no power to evict him. We ask to see a copy of this lease, and he says he doesn't keep it in the house but will get it to me soon, and assures me he won't be leaving. I tell him we will see him in court. He says he's quite sure my mother has no intention of kicking him out. I tell him she asked us to get him out of the house. He says, "Oh, I seriously doubt that." He smiles. It's the emptiest, falsest smile I have ever seen.

Eviction takes time. We can't stay around, though. My time off work is limited; we have to go home. First thing in the morning, back on the road. We will be driving home without Barbara. We still have no idea how to rescue her. As we leave North Carolina, a song comes on the radio: Gotye's *Somebody That I Used to Know*. I laugh and I cry and I cry again. It's the most fitting thing ever. My relationship with my mother feels exactly like a bad breakup.

LESSON LEARNED

I got sick about a week after I turned eighteen. My mother told me I would have to pay for the doctor on my own, since I was an official "adult" and she had removed me from her health insurance. I didn't know she'd planned to take me off her plan the very day I turned eighteen, but when she told me she had, I believed her. When she told me it would probably cost about five hundred dollars to see a doctor, I believed that too. So I didn't go. I just got sicker and sicker and sicker.

Every time I said anything about it, she told me it was too bad she couldn't help but I did have to take care of myself now that I was grown up. I did have savings, but not the five hundred she said it would probably cost. "Plus the follow-up visits, Cass. You really should have gotten yourself some health insurance, but it's too late now." My mother (and Bernard) watched as I became the sickest I have ever, ever been. Eventually, after about six weeks of this, I simply staggered into the living room and collapsed on the floor, weeping.

My mother said "Well, do you want to go to the hospital? It's going to be very expensive, I'm afraid."

I continued weeping. My mother asked if I had money to pay for the hospital. I shook my head, and wept on and on.

Bernard said, "She *has* to go, Barbara, look at her."

They took me to the ER, where it was discovered that I had an advanced kidney infection and a raging case of Septicemia. My fever was well over 104 (it had been for days) and I was very near death. "Whatever possessed you to let this go on so long?" they asked, and I told them I didn't have the money to see a doctor. They rolled their eyes at me.

My mother talked about the thousands and thousands of dollars this hospital visit was going to cost me. I was so worried about the bill. She kept showing me my chart, talking about the charges. "Look. They're charging you fifty dollars for that Tylenol they gave you." I stopped asking for things, thinking I might save a few dollars. I was there for five or six days, and the moment I felt even slightly better I started clamoring to be let out. (Every night is another thousand bucks, Cass, you better get well soon.)

The day I was being released, I asked in worried tones about the bill. The nurse said, "Oh, well, the insurance covered this of course, dear, so don't worry about that. You just get well and come back for your follow up."

I glared at my mother. She shrugged. "Well, Cass, yes, you were on my plan, obviously; I never did take you off. I only said I had taken you off because it will happen eventually, and I wanted you to be prepared for it. This was a lesson you needed to learn." She was quite sniffy about it.

"But I almost *died*," I wailed. She snorted at me. "Oh for crying out loud, Cass, I wasn't letting you *die*, don't be so *dramatic*. If you got sick enough I'd have taken you to the doctor, of course."

Which... well, that was a lie, wasn't it? Because I should have been taken to a doctor weeks and weeks before I did get taken – and even that day, my mother was prepared to just leave me writhing around on the filthy carpet until I agreed to pay for the medical care I so-obviously needed. If Bernard had not put his foot down (surely he knew, all along, about the insurance, about the lesson?) it's very likely I *would* have died, perhaps within a day or two.

When they had asked, in the hospital, "whatever possessed you to let this go on so long?" ... were they talking to me? Or were they, possibly, talking to my idiot mother?

I almost died (on that same filthy carpet) a few months later when my mother convinced me to dry-swallow not one but two large multivitamin pills, to show off for my visiting grandmother who fretted over her inability to swallow even the daintiest of tablets. I almost choked to death. But I managed to calmly walk to the kitchen and gulp water from the tap before I lost consciousness, and neither Nana nor my mother noticed.

COURT

My uncle agrees to take over the eviction case. He has to transport a car from Florida anyway, so he decides to fly to Florida, then drive up to Asheville and home from there in the car. I can't take the time off work, so my husband goes with him. Uncle Bob is a dedicated runner, so he's up at dawn – he's entered a 5k run. My husband sips coffee in a café and waits. He strikes up a conversation with a woman in the coffee shop; it turns out she's a retired lawyer, and she wants to get us some help because The Barbara Situation sounds pretty bad. She calls the lawyer she used to work with; it's the 4th of July, so he's not at work, but he directs another lawyer in the firm to contact us. Now we have two lawyers on our side: my uncle and this new guy.

We will make good use of them both, though the eviction case is pretty simple: our little thief has drawn up a "life lease" on the house that allows him to stay in the house until my mother's death. He had left himself the house along with all her belongings in the will he drew up for her to sign, so he thinks he's set for life on that score. But my mother lied to him, and he doesn't know that her husband, who co-owns the house, is still alive. Her husband did not sign this lease. Derrick insists that my mother is a widow, so the Judge calls a recess and goes to chambers, where he easily finds out the truth. She has a living husband; the lease is invalid. Derrick has thirty days to vacate the house and turn over the keys.

He glares at my uncle and tells him 'I'll see you again' and 'this isn't over' as he stalks out of the courtroom. And that is true. This is far from over.

While they are there, my husband and uncle look into places that might accept Barbara. Slim pickings, but they get her on a tentative waiting list at a couple of places. The one that is likeliest to be available first is run-down, according to my husband. It's a very old building. I say that will suit her fine; she prefers old buildings. It's the truth. But run-down or not, it will cost ten grand a month and before they can truly consider our request, she has to be formally accepted by Medicaid.

The people at Social Security tell us that this usually takes several weeks, but due to the nature of The Barbara Situation, they will try to push it through faster.

THE EXORCISM

After the Thanksgiving incident with the knives and the attempted stabbing, my mother called on some priests to exorcise the demon Sylvia from her house. They actually came, I couldn't believe it. She had just decided to become a Hindu. (She said she liked their vibe better, and the statues were cooler. I shit you not.) The priests who came to exorcise the house were not pleased with her – she had told them she was a Christian. Devout, she had said. Well, she'd had to say that, had she not, if she wanted them to come. So she, tanked up on wine, called up some Catholic churches at random until one of them agreed to send out exorcists. When they got there, they wanted to do prayers.

"Oh, no, don't be silly, I'm a Hindu. We don't pray like that. Go ahead if you want to, though. I don't really mind." The priests looked around as if for hidden cameras. This was so unexpected I felt a little sorry for them. Ma'am, they said. Miss, er... Missus... er. This is a Christian ceremony. It's all about calling on Christ. You have to be Christian or we can't do this.

Oh, no, Hindu is fine. Hindu is all the religions. So it's true, I am Christian, because Hindu encompasses everything. It's all good – go for it, exorcise that puppy. She really said this.

"That isn't the way this works."

The priests hammered at her for about an hour, refusing to do anything for her until she "accepted Christ" as her Savior. So she finally rolled her eyes and accepted Christ as her savior. I was laughing at the whole situation: what my mother needed exorcised from her house was the demon wine. Her demons were well-known to me, and had been for years. I followed them as they went from room to room, doing their thing. The priests with their Bibles and their Holy water. My drunk mother, fretting fearfully, wringing her hands, casting terrified glances at the closet where the demon-box of demon-masks was demon-kept, shuddering dramatically for effect. Blah blah blah. Despite having assured them over and over that she accepted Christ before they would start, as they left she told them again that she really was just more of a Hindu than a Christian, but that it was ok because Hinduism is all-encompassing. Which is exactly what I knew she would do. Of course.

Those priests looked scandalized. But what did they expect, really? She was obviously drunk, drunk when she called them, drunk when she answered the door... actively drinking the entire time they were there doing the Lord's work for her. Wake up, I wanted to shout. Wake up, guys – the demon is standing right here! She's gulping wine out of a classy, classy wine glass.

Shortly after this, my mother moved away. She asked if I would like to take possession of the disturbed kid's belongings, because she didn't have room for them anymore and felt bad throwing them out. I said no.

GETTING HER MOVED

We get the call from the Social Security offices; our claim has been approved. They have determined that she has, indeed, been taken advantage of. We notify the home and prepare to move Barbara. The timing is good; a room has just opened up for her. My husband flies out to handle it. My mother obviously likes my husband now, but he isn't sure she knows who he is in relation to her. When I was there with him, she seemed to know he was my husband, but sometimes I think she thought he was her brother. Her mind is full of holes. One time she said "one of her husbands" had repaired the roof, but when I asked her if it was Lorenzo who did that (it was), she looked at me blankly. She didn't know who Lorenzo was. Nor did she react to the mention of Bernard. But John, she remembered him. My father. Sometimes, I think she may believe my husband is John.

Concerned that she won't place his face correctly and will fuss, I arm him with mementoes to take. Maybe they will help, I think. I send him with some of her favorite Kliban cartoons, and some cartoons she, herself, drew before I was born. I send him with green chile sauce and with perfume she used to wear. I send him with pictures of me. She recognizes the pictures and seems to adore my husband. He tells me over the phone she appears to be very glad to see him. (I laugh; she probably thinks he, too, is her real son.) She recognizes nothing else I have sent, does not laugh at the cartoons. I cry to know that; one thing we truly had in common was our sense of humor.

Paul has rented a convertible, and he delivers her to her new room in it. He offers her a cigarette and drives her with the top down, her hair fluttering in the breeze. He says she enjoyed that a great deal. When he got her to the new place, she was angry that it wasn't her old house. She says, incensed, "you might have told me it was just another hospital."

Paul leans over and tells her "I did." She accepts this, mollified. She knows she doesn't remember anything.

He is in town another few days, hoping he will have the keys so he can check on the house, but he doesn't have them by the time he leaves.

FICKLE MOTHER GREAT AND SMALL

First there were dogs, then there were horses, then there was me. And after me came other things. My mother never did anything in a small way. We had mice by the hundreds. We raised them, supposedly for fun. They were cute. Habitrails all over the place and mice, mice, mice. We sold the pinkies to pet stores to offset the costs of raising them and to have somewhere for them to go, because we discovered that a mouse here and a mouse there shortly become mice everywhere. Soon we were selling grown mice as well as pinkies.

We delivered mice to pet stores in paper bags. Not the best plan, really. One time, we got to the store too early and needed to kill some time until the manager was there, so we went to the theater where my grandmother worked – still there as of this writing, a tiny little art theater called The Guild. We took the mice in with us because it was too hot in the car for them. *Don't tell your Nana there are mice in this bag.* And after the movie, we had a bag with a hole in it. *Don't ever, ever tell your Nana about this, Cass, she'll quit her job.* Poor Nana, she was utterly terrified of mice. I never breathed a word of it.

My mother's favorite mouse was a big golden male she named *Bestioso*. He was a mean mouse, and attacked the other males. But he was a glorious animal with testicles the size of grapes. You never expect mice to look like that. We had lots of mice with names, but I remember only two of them: Bestioso and Domino.

Domino was my favorite. He was black, with five white dots on his back, just like a domino. Domino was a fabulous pet. He sat on my arm and read books with me, he nibbled on my ears. He sat up to be petted. Then one day I squeezed him too hard – if you squeeze mice a little, I discovered, their eyes would bulge. It amazed me, so I squeezed him often, to see that happen. (Hey, I was only six or so, I wasn't trying to hurt him, I was just curious about the effect.) So, one day I squeezed him too hard, and he let me know it was too hard by biting me. I immediately apologized to him; I knew it was my own fault. I went to wash my finger off, and I mentioned it in an offhand way to my mother: wow, I squeezed Domino too hard and he bit me, haha. No biggie, I won't be doing that again, I said. But my mother told me he was a dangerous animal now that he had a taste for blood, and she made me put him outside to be a wild mouse. I am sure he didn't survive a week.

Later, when we were bird people, a friend gave me a parakeet. Ouch – my parakeet was named Ouch – was pigeon toed, which had rendered him useless for sale or breeding, and was why my mother's friend gave him to us free of charge. Ouch was a green beauty who sat on my books and took bites out of every page as I turned it. I adored him, but when he bit me, again... taste of blood, dangerous animal, better off in the wild... out he went. And again, I knew it was a death sentence. You'd think I'd have learned from the thing with

Domino never to tell my mother anything.

When my father died I found a photo album, a huge green book that had pages and pages and pages of photos of my mother with dogs, and then with horses. And then a few with infant me. And then nothing. Blank page after blank page. Because first there were dogs, and then there were horses. And then there was me. And after me, there were other things, but no time to patiently pin them down in books. That's one reason why it's so hard to ever start a story where the story starts, maybe. Because the real story is the loss of control. We don't have any pictures of the mice. Only one or two of the birds.

When I go through my mother's basement years later looking for anything of value, I will find her first cherished antique birdcage crushed under a pile of boxes.

THE HOUSE

The weasel gives up the keys only after several demands. Our lawyer in North Carolina gets us in touch with a good estate auctioneer, we get details on what will be required. He and Bob start working on the case against our conman – we have some evidence that he preys on elderly women, and has had more than one family home given over to him for virtually nothing.

I tell the legal team what my mother told me years ago: she met this man one night in 2008 when she was walking home alone from the wine store. She told me then that she had met a very handsome man who was incredibly rich, and said that he had picked her up on the street near her home thinking she was a prostitute. She said they had a good laugh about that, and then went to her house for a drink. She also told me they considered sleeping together, but it would have been too "weird".

She also said he told her he was a recovering crack addict and that his name changed depending on his mood. She had told me all this on the phone, because shortly after she started spending time with this man, he took her computer for repairs and never brought it back, so she no longer had email.

Our other contact in town is a former friend of his, who

has grown terrified of him. This friend is the one who contacted me, in fear that my mother might be dead in the basement. The one who called every nursing home and found her for us. He's afraid to go near the house, because he thinks Derrick will be waiting to ambush him. But now that we have the keys, we need someone to check the house and make sure it hasn't been trashed. The lawyer can do it, of course, but the fees would be extensive.

Brett reluctantly agrees to check the house, asks me if there is anything I am looking for in particular. I don't really know what I am looking for. A better mother maybe. I tell him there is one item of jewelry that means something to me, and I describe it. I think maybe Derrick won't have stolen it because it doesn't look very valuable. I can't begin to explain why I value it.

We're told at some point that the house alarm has been triggering alerts since Derrick turned off the electricity, and the woman who was named as the emergency contact lives here in Albuquerque – she can't do anything about the alarm. I know this woman; I've had her telephone number memorized since I was four years old.

F

They say, when you write the capital letter F, a rising top bar means you want to improve yourself, and if the top bar extends over the whole word you are inclined to be protective. I write my F backwards. I do that because that's the way Floy did it when she signed her name. She signed it many times on birthday cards to me, and on letters to my mother. I was entranced by Floy, who had secrets I never did discover, two grown daughters I adored just from hearing about them, and a cat that was so amazingly cool, I've never forgotten him. (Later, when we look her up, she will ask me if I remember her Louie. She won't believe me when I tell her I named my own orange Tabby after hers.)

Floy was my preschool teacher. Even back then, she was *the* emergency contact. If my mother was caught with a drink in her hand, I should immediately run to the neighbor's house and call my father at work. If he wasn't there, I was to call Floy. I recited her address and number as often as I did my own, from the time I was four. And it did not need to be an obvious drink. A bottle of liquor was clearly cause for alarm, but if I saw her with a glass of juice or water I should always sniff it. In fact, I was encouraged to come sip from any drink she had in her hand, and if she so much as flinched when I reached for the glass, I was to run to the neighbors and call either my father or Floy, or both of them. If I said my mother had been drinking, Floy or my father would rush to me like the house was on fire. All I would need to say was that my mother wouldn't let me sip from her drink, and they would fly to me, sirens blaring.

And the cause for all of this was that my mother had battled a very bad drinking problem, and she said it would never get better. She was and always would be an alcoholic, and one drink meant she would become a monster. She said she would try to stop me running out to the neighbor's, so I had to be fast. If she caught me, she said, it would be very bad. She told me she would try to kill me.

When my mother told me she would become a monster, I didn't believe her.

FLOY DOESN'T TRUST ME

We contact Floy, drive to her house, give her a copy of my published book, and a copy of the kindergarten project we did in 1970. She's glad to see me, if only because I can make the alarm company leave her alone, but she seems suspicious of me when I tell her what's been going on. I know why; when my father died, my mother told her friend (I believe she told all her friends this) that I inherited *billions* of dollars, and that I became, essentially, a bitch. This is the primary excuse she gave her friends for leaving town – to get away from me and my bad rich-girl attitude.

Floy hasn't seen my mother in years either, but has been phoning regularly. She says, "Well, your mother was certainly very angry with you, Cassie, I know that. After your father died… well." I tell her that story is not true, that I did not inherit billions or even millions of dollars. I remind her about my mother's drinking problem, which I'm sure Floy was well aware of at one time. But she seems not to have a full grasp of it, clearly has no idea how serious the problem was. My mother had managed to hide this pretty well for a long, long time. Floy is aware that my mother drank, of course. But she's got no real frame of reference for it. Floy is one of the soberest people I ever met. I wonder if she ever knew I had her phone number memorized for emergencies, or what the emergency my mother had in mind back then was. I tell her now, but she looks at me as though she does not believe me.

She says she knows my mother wanted to give everything to Derrick. "She was very fond of this young man, Cass. She told me he was her 'real' son." I roll my eyes. Floy doesn't realize how many 'real' sons my mother claimed to have. I tell her again, it was the drinking. Derrick brought her the only thing that really mattered to her: Wine. When nobody else could or would do it, he was there. This is why she called him her real son. This is why she is so fond of him.

Floy nods, somewhat accepting my knowledge, though clearly she doesn't trust me. She loves my mother dearly, that's obvious. She says she doesn't understand why Lorenzo got my mother drinking again. But it wasn't Lorenzo who did that. Doesn't she remember it was Bernard? But maybe she's forgotten Bernard. Indeed, mention of Bernard earns me only another suspicious and confused frown.

On request, we give Floy the number for Barbara's place so she can call her. We tell her she shouldn't talk with Derrick because we are involved in a lawsuit against him. We tell her we have explained the situation to the people at this new home, and that we have requested that they not permit Derrick to visit.

That afternoon, Floy calls my mother and tells her we have stopped Derrick from visiting her. When my mother expresses desire to see Derrick, Floy explains she has every right to request of the nurses that he be allowed in to visit. So of course she asks for that. Fucking Floy.

ANOTHER REAL SON

As a very small girl, in Mexico, on the nude beach, I played with a young boy named David. He was a couple of years younger than I was, but about the same size. As I recall he was pretty much the only child other than myself in the general group. I liked him. He was incredibly quiet. David's father was black and his mother was white, and this was the early seventies so it was something of a big deal. My mother said they were very good friends of ours. At the end of our vacation, my mother told me that David's parents had asked if we'd like to adopt him. She asked me if I would like David to come home with us. I had always wanted a brother, hadn't I? Sure, I said.

So we took him. I kid you not, we put that little boy in our truck and took him back to the States with us, and we told everyone he was adopted. My mother told me he was her son just as much as I was her daughter, and he was my real brother. Her real son. My mother had his ear pierced. And when he hit his head on the table hard, and we discovered him hiding, huge silent tears rolling down his face, we took him to the emergency room and told *them* he was adopted. My mother told us both to not say anything about him having any other parents, he was adopted, he was my brother, I was his sister, this is all perfectly legal. The doctors treated him. On the way out, we saw a policeman, and my mother whispered to us again to be really quiet and not to draw the attention of the fuzz. So, naturally, when we passed the cop, David blurted out "Hi, Fuzz!" I will never forget it. But the cop barely glanced at us, and when we got to the car we all laughed. Except David. David almost never laughed about anything. He almost never smiled. Just quiet, quiet, all the time. And when he cried, those big silent tears.

My mother had a photographer friend take a number of photos of the two of us. David was holding a carrot in about half of the photos. My father snatched the carrot away and threw it in the weeds. Paying for these professional photos, he said, and this damn half-eaten carrot in all of them. David is smiling a rare smile in a few of the photos. After my dad threw the carrot away, he stopped smiling.

I still have the photos. I also have a charcoal sketch of the two of us. I remember it like it was yesterday, having this done. David cried as usual the entire time. The poor artist, he kept trying to find ways to make David smile. My mother told him it was just the way he was, and to sketch the truth. Eventually, the sketch-artist finished up with him – somber, sad, worried David. If you didn't know how it had been, you might not even notice it: the artist took my mother at her word, and he sketched the tear in David's eye. It's subtle, but we (my mother and I both) thought it was brilliant. David had nothing to say.

David lived with us for several months. I really believed he was there forever, and I think he did too, because when his parents came to collect him about nine or ten months later, he cried. He left a lot of his toys behind, because obviously he didn't think he was never coming home again.

Jesus, people. He was three when we got him and four when he left. What the fuck was wrong with you, telling him you were his real mother for all those months? And me, telling me that too... that he was your kid just as much as I was... and then giving him back as though that had always been the plan? As though he really didn't mean much at all? As though, to be honest, you were glad to be rid of him?

She never mentioned him again in the context of wondering how he was or where he was or what he was doing. She did, however, mention the whole affair frequently in terms of how we had once "adopted" a black kid. So woke right? Always remember how not-racist we are: we adopted a black boy! I had a black brother! Never forget that! But when I was much older and asked ...where is he now? Oh, Cass, his parents were on drugs all the time, he's probably dead or in jail. That was when I found out that my parents weren't good friends of his parents at all – they'd only met them that week on the beach. And they had some trouble they were running from, so that was why they had wanted him to come with us for a while. And it was always the plan that they were going to take him back.

They came again, several years later, just to visit. David was just as quiet as ever, but much taller. I was around nine or ten then, so he'd have been seven, eight. He collected the toys he'd left behind. He had a baby sister, I forget her name. He said almost nothing the whole visit, but when they packed up to leave he had those big, quiet tears. My mother said he had thought he'd be allowed to stay.

I never saw him again. I've looked on social media, but I didn't find him. Indeed, maybe dead or in jail by now. Under the circumstances, I wouldn't be surprised.

ASHEVILLE AGAIN

We make another trip, this time to arrange for the eventual sale of the house and furnishings, such as they are. We fly out, and rent a Ryder truck for the return trip, so we can bring some of the items back with us – though we are not certain what those items will be.

We stay, again, at the hotel near her home. We've grown fond of this place, though this time there is some snafu and they want us to stay in one room for the first two nights and then move to another room for the rest of the stay, because they have promised another group that they can stay in adjacent rooms and ours is one of these rooms. My husband refuses to do this, and for the rest of the stay I am well aware that the people next door know we have inconvenienced them. They sit on the patio outside their room smoking cigarettes and drinking beer, glaring at us. They think we are pricks. I am too stressed out to care.

Her house, now devoid of Derrick and his growling dogs, feels more familiar to me. It looks, in fact, like she could be living there. The old couch is gone, replaced with some new strange piece that I have never seen. We were told the couch had been irreparably damaged due to her incontinence, and I don't doubt it. It's a shame, because it was an antique, and she was quite fond of it. I don't care about that, but am saddened by the fact she has also destroyed the wing-back chair of my grandmother's. Nana had promised me that chair, but my mother held it hostage against me. She had called me several years previous and told me she was probably going to have to pay a fortune to have it reupholstered, asked what color I wanted it to be, as it was "my" chair. I said I didn't care. I suspected at the time she was lying, had no plans to recover the chair, and was just trying to get me to offer to chip in money for the project. I knew, even then, I was likely never to see it again anyway. But I loved that chair, and it is gone. It was probably taken to the dump with the old antique couch.

Paul marks off a section of floor with tape – this is the size of the truck. We can take with us what will fit in this taped-off area. He is expecting that I will fill it up rapidly and pine over items I cannot fit, but I know what space we have at our own house, on the other end. I look at everything in the house and weep over much of it, but I select very few items, overall, to take.

I take with me the library table that I have always loved. It was a much-used desk when I was a child. She left it behind when we moved from my childhood home, left behind a lot of things she later demanded my father return to her. He eventually gave her all the things she asked for: the antique chest, the beautiful old black sideboard she fought him tooth and nail over, this library table. Once she got it, it was our kitchen table for years. Later, she used it as a desk again. It was her desk and computer table here, too, apparently, though there is no computer with it.

Though this table is here, the sideboard and other cherished items are not. We've been told there is a storage unit; I've asked Bob to please get in touch with the storage place and explain what's happening, so we won't lose what's there. I doubt any of these things are there, though. They were valuable, and probably have been sold. I am hopeful, though, that some items will be hiding there. Maybe the painting my grandmother did, the one of the roses she had to paint three times because everyone in the family wanted one. Nana's flimsy tea trolley is here, so I take that. It's not worth much; I remember when she bought it at the mall, it's not old. But because I remember it, there is sentimental value. She used to keep her Hurricane Lamps on it. Those were valuable. Of course, those – inherited by my mother – are gone, as is her old clock. There is another childhood clock here, an old mantel clock, but it's broken. It always was. I don't bother climbing the ladder to retrieve it. I find my grandmother's Buddha statue. His fan is missing, but I take him anyway. I rub his belly and tell him I am sorry, so sorry. My mother's Ganesha smiles serenely at us both: change is inevitable, he says.

On the coat rack, I see my mother's khaki parka, the one that was new when I was six, the day we made snow angels. I leave it behind. It would only make me cry.

CLEVER FOXES,
BEARS FOR STRENGTH

When I was little, I was taught that I was never allowed to call anyone an Aunt or Uncle unless they were literally my aunt or uncle. This limited my Aunt and Uncle experience considerably. If my mother hadn't permitted certain great-aunts and uncles into the mix, I would have had only two uncles and aunts!

I was very sad to know I could never be an aunt myself, as I have no siblings. My mother told me if I wanted to be an aunt, I would have to marry someone with brothers and sisters, so I could be an aunt by marriage. It was my only hope. Then I married a man with no siblings, dooming myself. Forever aunt-hoodless. (But rules, you know. Mothers, and mine in particular, don't always get things right. So for all the people who today call me Aunt Cass even though I am not: thank you! You've righted a wrong, there.)

I had only one grandparent: my mother's mother, Vera, whom I called Nana. I loved her and I spent time with her whenever I could. Nana took me to a bead store once. It was some crafts project she was working on for her sorority, I think. Nana was big on her sorority; I inherited all her old sorority badges and pins. Why I kept them, I have no idea, maybe because she was so proud of them. Anyway, I don't remember what the project was, but I remember the bead store. I was amazed by it. So many beads! So many wonders! I wanted all of them, but Nana allowed me to select only a few. Five beads or maybe ten. Just to keep me occupied. I played with those beads for the rest of my stay. Good deal: a dollar worth of beads kept me entertained for days. I would have been about seven.

When I came home from that visit beads were all I talked about. The ones I had, the ones I had seen, the ones Nana bought, her bead project, on and on I went. You know how kids babble, and I was ever a babbler. It annoyed my mother, the babbling. Also the fact that Nana had done something so simple and made such an impression. "Well, Cass," my mother said. "Beads aren't that hard to find. Anyone can buy some beads." After some reflection, she added. "Actually I've been thinking about making a necklace myself. We'll go buy some beads next weekend, how about that?"

I was ecstatic. Beads! Yes, yes, more beads. And though I had my grandmother's bead store in mind, my mother took me to a different bead store. I will admit this now: one of these bead stores was in Old Town, and one was not, and I don't remember which one was which. They were both fabulous, though. Beads upon beads, row after row, box after box after box of every color and shape bead one could imagine.

My mother motioned for me to follow. "We're going to make a heishei fetish necklace," she said. "Help me choose." Foxes? Of course. Crows? Yes, please. And bears? Certainly, bears. What color? All the colors, and yes to everything, everything, I wanted all of them. I wanted a turtle, too. My mother added a frog to the mix. Then she selected some turquoise beads and coral ones, and then some others. I think those were oyster shell. On the way home, she talked about how each of the animals we selected held special meaning for the native tribes. They would bring good health and prosperity. Especially the crows, she said, would be very good for us.

When we got home, we laid the beads out on the table and she designed the necklace. Shall we put crow, fox, crow, bear? Or shall we, better, put bear, crow, fox, bear? We arranged them a few different ways. How about the turtle in the middle? But then where the frog? And conversely, frog in the middle leaves turtle hanging out like an afterthought. We must make sure the turtle and frog each hold a special place, equal to each other! In the end, the lone turquoise fox was selected for the center, the lowest point of the necklace, and we put the toad and frog on the left and right a few inches up, so they were both prominently displayed. The other animals were pretty randomly placed, bear, bear, fox, bear, bird, no apparent pattern or order.

It was the most beautiful necklace I had ever, ever seen.

SEARCHING THE HOUSE
IN ASHEVILLE

There is no paperwork to be found anywhere in the house. We are looking for her identification cards; we are still trying to move her to Albuquerque but she's too incontinent for a three-day drive and though she is now so out of it we could probably wheel her into a plane, we can't get her on a plane without ID.

I stand in the hall for a long while, looking at a picture there. I was always fond of it. It's of a man in a Persian outfit of some sort, I think. I have never known. My mother and Bernard bought this at an auction. The frame was damaged; my mother spent hours repairing it, hoping it could become valuable. She had taken a dowel, from the hardware store, and carefully fitted a piece into this frame. Then she took wood putty, and smoothed it over the cracks, sanded and stained it. But the damage was too bad, the item was worthless and they were unable to sell it. It's hardly noticeable, but I know where to look. It's there, still. Why this should surprise me, I can't imagine, but it does. The damage is still exactly as it was when I last saw this thing. My husband asks me what I am doing, and I tell him I am looking at the painting. He tells me we haven't got room for stupid paintings and to hurry up and get busy with the furniture. That probably should surprise me. It doesn't. I leave the painting alone, and still regret not taking it. I was the one who chose the correct size dowel for the repair job.

I go through the books. The ones I want are gone. I throw a random selection of books into a box. The glass-fronted bookcase has a broken panel. Years and years, I was so careful, we were always so careful not to break it. Now it's broken, and I can't be sure it was an accident.

In the basement, where I expect to find... I don't know what. Robert De Niro maybe, cans of green chile, perhaps old suitcases or tools... what I find is a total jumble of nonsense. Tools, of course, by the shitload – Lorenzo left in too much of a hurry to take them. Also mildew. The basement flooded when the water heater leaked, and there is black mold on every surface. It reeks of mold down here. There are piles of moldy books, moldy boxes. We don't want to go through them. I poke around as well as I can considering the mess.

There is a lamp there – we bought the lamp at a flea market, but the shade was new, from Sears. It bored my mother, so she bought a roll of Burgundy fringe and glued a row around the base. The remaining few feet of fringe was mine to use as I wished. It was so precious to me that I rarely did cut a snip of it off for anything, but I did use a few inches of it making finger puppets when I was in the tenth grade. I forget what I did with the rest eventually, but it is gone now. I yearn to reach that lamp and take it. My husband says it's all way too moldy to handle, to leave it be. I can't explain: not the lamp, the fringe, the *fringe*. It's moldy, too, certainly. I cannot climb over all the wet disarray anyway. But I just want to touch it, the little time machine that I know it is.

(Months later I will find similar fringe at WalMart and just stroke it with both hands for about ten minutes until the floor-walkers start eyeing me up for a loony.)

The time machines are everywhere, ruined bits of my life, coming back through time to remind me who I was once, and where I had been then. Where we were, when we were together. When these were the precious things we coveted, the things we called our own.

I see many old bed frames, heavy iron castaways. She and Bernie bought these antiques at auctions. I remember watching her delicately gilding (by hand!) the highlights onto the flowers. I can see the gilding from across the basement. There's the bed my mother and Bernard shared. Look, that's probably the very mattress. And there, look, I say. See that little bed? That was my bed. That's the bed where I lost my virginity.

On the porch, among the boxes of old junk and clothes, we find the smoker my mother used to cook the turkey we fed to people at our wedding reception. We also find a photo album. It's filled with pictures of Lorenzo's family, but because it also contains pictures of me I suspect it may have been Bernard's photo album, left behind when he moved away, then packed by Lorenzo when he and my mother moved to North Carolina. He wouldn't have known it wasn't my mother's. He might have assumed it was my own. It's a time capsule, like everything here is. I see a picture of Bernard working on a dresser in front of the trailer he lived in when he first came into our lives. He was The Chair Doctor then, when he was our boarder. In this picture, the neighbor girls and I are all watching. My mother must have taken the picture. She left my father for this fool, I think. I remember loving him dearly, though: this fool who didn't know my mother left my father to be with him. There are other pictures of Bernard, pictures of me circa 1977. Pictures of Lorenzo and his first family, and of me with them, for we were friends with Lorenzo's family years before we were related by marriage.

An eye is painted on the porch wall nearby, with lettering: You are not living the right life. We are told later that my mother painted that there. With mixed feelings, I take the photo album.

In the kitchen, hanging on the window latch, I find the fetish necklace. Most of the beads are broken.

OUR MARRIAGE GIFT

My husband and I were married at The Press Club. It's a lovely old house with a lot of history. They have a bar, where they sell liquor. They get around the licensing requirements by being a "members only" establishment. They get around that by having people who want to hold events there sign in (every one of them) as a guest of the manager.

It's a great downtown wedding venue, with a gorgeous *en suite* park. They have several floors, the bottom of which has a game room with a pool table. After our wedding in the park, we retired to the Club where I served enough food for three hundred people, had champagne toasts, cake, the works. We had the exclusive use of the property until five, when they opened the club to regular members. I left the remaining (several) trays of food for the use of the regular members, and my husband and I went downstairs to play pool with a few close friends. We left my mother and Lorenzo at the bar. I don't know what time they left the event. What I do know is that we were presented with a bar tab well in excess of eight hundred dollars. The bartender, mildly amused by our dismay, said my mother had ordered several rounds of drinks for the house, all on our tab. And wine, he told us. Of course, wine, for herself. Many, *many* glasses. Yes, yes, quite a large tab. Oh teehee, quite an evening. Oh haha, what a hoot she is. But of course he had no way of knowing, did he, said the barkeep. He assumed my mother had the rights to place orders on our tab. We had, after all, ordered her first drink for her, and put it on our tab, had we not? We should have made our wishes more plain.

Among the gifts we opened later, we found that she and Lorenzo had given us a 500.00 check as a wedding gift. She mentioned this largesse almost every time she saw me over the next few years. She never once acknowledged having more than a single glass of wine at our wedding. If that much, really. They'd left early, she told me. They had certainly left the very moment we went downstairs, of course.

The club regretted every penny of that tab later, when Barbara bought a membership to the Club and became a regular. They got their turn with Barbara, and they deserved every moment of it.

MAMA PAJAMAS

We visit Barbara again, bringing some pajamas and slippers and a stuffed dog. We put up a few things for her from the house: some Hindu masks and a Buddha. She seems confused by these but loves the dog. She pets it, seems to think it's a real dog. Early on, I thought she was putting me on when she acted feeble-minded, but now I know better. She is serious when she says she worries the dog won't get enough food, and that he will get lost without a leash.

He does, in fact, because one of her new neighbors roams the halls all hours, stealing everything he can get his hands on. "Poppy" was discovered to have walked away with another resident's dentures; they found them secreted in the tank of his toilet. He steals her dog several times while we are there. I worry he may steal the small television we put in her room, but one can only do so much. We paint her name on the back of the television, and write it into her new pajamas; everything she has bears her name, the name of a man she doesn't remember. Every month, they hold a yard sale here in the hallway, selling items the residents have lost or left behind. They can't keep all this stuff straight. They promise to do their best. I believe them; they are kind people, doing an impossible job. In the hallway, they have inexplicably hung many little barrel monkeys as decorations.

Barbara asks me where we are staying while we are in town. We talk about the hotel. We talk over the top of her, like she is a child. When we mention concern that the house will be empty, she lights up. She has a friend, his name is Derrick, and he could watch the house while we are gone. We tell her again that he is no friend.

They've cut her nails, to keep her from hurting herself. She didn't want them cut; fought them the whole time, we are told. As a reward, they allowed her to paint them. She chose pink. Pink! I goggle at the nails and laugh. But of course, she is beyond the joke. I was never allowed to wear pink as a little girl, no matter how I begged. Pink was the embodiment of sexism. Nails were meant to be red, my mother always told me. Red, like bloody claws. For my mother, everything should be red or purple; bright, slashing, furious, bold attacks of color. I ask her, for fun, what she thinks of her nails now. She says they are nice, but too short. They cut them off, she tells me. She looks bereft. But the pink? Oh, I love that, she says. Isn't it pretty? She waggles the short, tame claws, smiling innocently again. They are still much longer than my own.

Later, we stop at the house for a final walkthrough. Brett comes with wine, and a fondue pot. He wants to toast her memory, remember her with fine cheeses. He needs this, for closure, I think. I spend some time looking out the windows into the so-called "back" yard, which is actually a steep, jungle-like hill that's virtually inaccessible. Brett says my mother claimed to have thrown all her guns back there, into the lush green. I wonder what else. There are books moldering in the side yard, trailing down the embankment like scree, and I see clothes there too.

I eat the cheese and drink the wine. It is good. I hate it.

OFFICER SOUP &
THE YEAR OF XANAX

Shortly after I was married, my mother and Lorenzo were in a minor car accident. My mother decided to use this as an excuse to become demanding and hysterical, which of course she did. She tried to sue the guy for millions, based on her complaint that she was so terrorized by the sight of a car now that she could not be out in one at all, and also that she could no longer fold her hands perfectly in the prayer pose for yoga. The fact that she did not practice yoga at all made no difference; she insisted that she had an absolute right to fold her hands that way at a moment's notice and the fact her wrist was now stiff was a hardship worth hundreds of thousands of dollars. Her lawyer – my uncle – told her straight up that this was not actionable and declined to pursue it (this was the beginning of the end for those two) but her doctor did prescribe her a big bottle of Xanax to help with the anxiety.

Now, what she did was continue to drink just gallons of wine, but also take lots of Xanax. This did relax her, I will say that much. She was very relaxed. Relaxed enough to act on every nutty whim she had. She first created an LLC to limit her liability. Then she bought a car. Then she forged Lorenzo's signature and cashed in his IRA and bought a house. (He declined to press charges against her, and they did sell that house right away for a profit so that worked out well.) Then she decided she should have her earlobes repaired. Years of wearing heavy brass earrings – mostly handmade by Bernard – had stretched her earlobes out so much that she could not wear normal earrings: you could have put a pencil through the holes in her ears. And since Lorenzo had proven himself to be a buyer of diamond rings and bracelets, probably she was thinking she should get earrings, too. While they were doing her earlobes, she had her eyeliner tattooed on. Naturally she came home from that looking like she'd been in a bar fight. The next evening she called the police and told them she was fighting with her husband and implied he had beaten her up. Then she called me to brag about how clever she was, making it look like Lorenzo was an abuser so she could take everything if they divorced. The officer who came to take her complaint was named Officer Campbell – but, she said, he told her that everyone called him "Soup".

When the police arrived, Lorenzo made it clear that she'd had the tattoos done the day before – and she was drunk, so the police took the report and left without making a fuss. But there was a "real" dispute on the record from some months earlier when they had both been drunk and fighting, so now there were two. I knew this was her plan. My mother had been bragging about her plan to have a record on file, the cops having to come for disputes all the time, so that she would have the upper hand in a divorce. And Lorenzo was still new to the Barbara Experience at that time – they'd been married only a few years then. He didn't take me too seriously when I warned him. He didn't believe the things I told him, the stuff she had done to Bernard, to me. It was not in his heart to hear it, not yet.

So, I called the police to give them the story. I asked for the officer they called Soup, and he did call me back. When I told him the things I have just told you, he also almost did not believe it. But then he asked me a question that helped my case considerably. Just casually, he asked me if I was the daughter who was in college.

I told him I was her only daughter and that I was not in college.

Hm, he said. Only daughter? My mother had told him she had a daughter in college that he should meet her because he and she would be perfect for each other. He had the impression she had two daughters. I thought (but did not say) I was surprised she hadn't mentioned a real son.

I reminded him again I was her only daughter and that I was not in college... and that I was married, though he did sound like a very nice man, haha... sorry to disappoint. You know, maybe some other life. One where I was the person my mother had dreamed of. (A son, perhaps. Or a daughter who had married someone she approved of. A daughter who had never left home. A daughter who had been tractable. The real daughter to match the real son.)

Officer Soup said "Ah. Now I think I see." He thanked me for clarifying the situation, agreed that yes, her plan could really prove to be a problem for her husband and said he was lucky to have me on his side.

ENDINGS

Back at home, we continue to work on our case against Derrick. The immediate problem is finding him in order to serve the paperwork. Brett discovers the venue where he plays guitar, and finds out what night he is expected there. He notifies the sheriff and they deliver the summons. Derrick slaps a lien on the house in response – one day before it would have been too late for him to do that, literally one day. Such is our luck. He claims he's been working tirelessly and at great expense to make repairs to the house. We are forced to compromise, so over the course of the next few weeks our lawyers haggle. In the end, we give him her car and drop the lawsuit in exchange for his dropping the lien. His claims are absurd but we can't afford to fight him at length; this has been an expensive process and we need to sell the house.

A day or two before the auction is scheduled, Brett calls to tell us the ceiling of the kitchen has fallen in and now lies atop the stove. Also, he says, one of the auctioneer's work crew took a huge dump in the unworking toilet. So, that happened. But we do sell the house eventually. We pay the lawyers and the other outstanding bills. And then Lorenzo gets his much-needed divorce, finally, after all these years. He is free at last.

I am not free yet.

THE RAPE-AND-BRACELET STORY

My mother's Xanax and Wine problem persisted for a while. My mother had paid for a membership to The Press Club – it was very near her house – and when Lorenzo did not agree to take her there, she took herself. One day she came home from the Press Club with some damage to the car, and the Press Club revoked her membership right after that. We never heard the whole story on that one. Shortly after that, my mother threw her diamond tennis bracelet into the bushes.

Now. Lorenzo knew she had the bracelet on, because she had imperiously demanded a wine refill and he had brought the bottle out to her on the patio swing where she was sitting. She was toying with the bracelet at the time, he noted. When she demanded wine again shortly after that, he saw it was gone. Where did your bracelet go? She would not say. She only glared at him. Well, it was expensive, obviously, so he looked around and found it in the bushes.

I could have told him it would be in the nearest bushes, because that was a thing my mother did. She drunkenly threw things into the bushes for attention or sport or whatever fucked-up reason... car keys, her gun, shoes... thousands of dollars in diamonds. So yes, fortunately, the bracelet was right there and he found it quickly. What he didn't know was how far my mother would take a thing like this. So she immediately told him she had not thrown it into the bushes but that a man had tried to steal it. And that during the struggle, the bracelet must have become loose and somehow been flung into the bushes. And then the man had run away. But she could never have known the bracelet was not in his pocket. Obviously. How very dare you accuse her of throwing it into the bushes when clearly she had been attacked? How very dare you not have her safety in mind? How very very darey darey you, any of you, ever suggesting that she might waste energy to throw, literally *throw* actual diamonds into the actual bushes, you horrible horrible man!

By the next morning, she was complaining that she had been not just robbed but also groped. In fact, the man who tried to steal her bracelet (before for some reason throwing it into the bushes and fleeing) had actually physically attacked her and tried to pull her clothes off. And Lorenzo, of course, had sat not three feet from it all, while she screamed and screamed and fought off this rapist with her bare hands, and he had noticed nothing. Nothing! What a horrible husband he was, to let her be attacked on the porch and virtually raped.

The next day, she claimed that she in fact *had* been raped. She called me repeatedly over the next couple of days to snivel about this attempted rape, but for what may by now be obvious reasons to you, dear reader, I was having none of it.

When I visited her a day or two after that, she was in bed on the telephone. She said "my daughter is here now, she is here now," and then "yes, yes, here she is" and she triumphantly handed the phone to me. "They want to talk with you," she said.

It was the Rape Crisis Center. They thought I was a devil. "Your mother has been through a terrible trauma –" the rape counsellor began. I cut her off. I told her my mother was not traumatized, that she was making the whole story up.

"Oh, yes, yes, she said that was the way you would react. It's simply terrible when victims of rape are not believed by members of their own family, it's dreadful when they cannot count on the support of loved ones, it's so unfair to the –"

"She's not a fucking victim, she made the story up! She was drunk and she threw her –"

"Oh we must never blame the victims, perhaps she had something to drink but that is not an excuse to rape someone, whether she was sober is not the issue, you should never ever shame a rape victim in this manner, you are behaving very badly, your mother needs support now and I have been on the phone with her for an hour, talking about how you and her husband refuse to believe her and this is just so wrong and so –"

"She made the whole thing up! There was no attack. She is doing this for attention, that's all. She's a drunk, you aren't getting the picture. She makes shit up."

"You are just like she said! This poor woman, rape victims deserve to be believed, and this is the worst sort of... My God! It was so hard for her to come forward with her story and you –"

My patience, thin already, was gone.

"You idiot – Listen, you are wasting valuable time that should be used for helping actual rape victims. She was sitting on the porch two feet from her husband and she was drunk and she threw her bracelet in the weeds and is now trying to pretend a rapist did it. There was no rapist. She is a drunk and a fabricator of tales. I am done with this and if you had sense you would be, too." I glared at my mother and handed her the phone. "There are real victims out there. And you know it." She glared back at me – but she did get off the phone.

I never heard another peep about the so-called rape. A few days after this, the police found a drunk Barbara wandering around in Taos with no shoes on. She had taken a taxi there, apparently.

SHAKESPEARE AND OSSOBUCO

We visit Asheville again a few months later. We make reservations at the usual hotel, but they call a few hours later and cancel them on us. We are no longer welcome at the crappy old hotel. They decline to offer us a reason. We suspect it is because we refused to change rooms on the last visit, but what can we do? We make reservations at the Aloft, which is a much nicer hotel, and it is here that we watch the Superbowl. To hell with the old hotel and its death-rattle elevator. My feelings are hurt, though.

At the home, my toothless, addle-pated mother is in good sprits. Indeed, she is more charming than I have ever known her to be. It's touching, almost – or would be, if I didn't want to smack her in the face because I am so angry with her. I have been angry for so long, I forget most people don't feel this way. The astonished looks I get from people at the way I talk about my mother are always a surprise to me. I suppose the astonished looks I give people when they talk about their sane and cherished parents are a surprise to them, too. I am a foreigner, my world is something other than theirs. And now my world also contains this new one with this new mother of mine.

In her closet, we discover the evidence of Derrick's most recent visit: he had brought her a Christmas stocking. Filled with what, I know not, but clearly nothing good. Very cheap chocolate-flavored bullshit is my guess, to please her ever-present sweet tooth. The stocking is empty. I stuff it into the garbage bin and spit on it. I curse. My mother blinks at me, no idea what I am saying or doing. She whines that her fruit is sour. I think it is watermelon. I tell her it is not sour, she just needs to eat it. She tries again, makes a face. This is *terrible* watermelon, she says. It turns out to be grapefruit. I am annoyed anew, but I have to laugh. My laughter makes her smile her toothless smile. I suddenly feel so much loss I can hardly stand it. But this train, rolling, rolls on. I roll with it, because there is no choice.

We distract ourselves as well as we can while we are there. We take in a Shakespeare show and we take Brett out to dinner. He orders Ossobuco, which comes with a tiny fork to eat the marrow with. I have never seen the like of it.

Two months ago, my uncle forgot to pay the past-due balance on the storage unit and they auctioned everything off. I will never know what was lost. In the middle of the night, I believe the whole world may have been in there.

THE WAY SHE LEFT

My mother decided, after waking up in a Taos jail, that Xanax did not go well with wine. She stopped taking the pills, but did not slow the wine consumption at all. She drank and drank and drank. And she became increasingly erratic and abusive of everyone around her. She said the only time she had ever once felt normal was when she took Xanax, and we had told her she was crazy then, so obviously she could never be normal, and she had to "self medicate" with wine alone. She was only doing what she had to do, she said, to stay alive without the meds which we wouldn't allow her to have.

She picked another fight with Lorenzo, and he broke her wrist while defending himself. She called me and told me he had broken her wrist. I did not believe her. I guess I should have, because he actually did break her wrist. But I assumed she had broken it herself. It was hard to know by this point what the truth was. She fell down so much. She diagnosed herself with Multiple Sclerosis and signed up for the free magazines. She had a priest come in to exorcise the house of Sylvia. She hired a fortune teller to come to the house and read her fortune in the crystals; he told her that I was the real problem in her life, that I was out to get her.

Then my father died. After having been divorced from him

for seventeen years – and having been remarried to Lorenzo for six – my mother became furious that my father had not left her anything in his will. He'd even had the nerve to leave his house to me, and to me alone. A few months later, when it became obvious that I was not going to suddenly give her this house, she abruptly announced she was moving across the country to North Carolina. And she did, immediately. She got on a train and went there, she located the house she wanted to buy, and she bought it. She never came back. She left Lorenzo behind to pack up the house here and arrange to get it on the market. She left Lorenzo behind to say all the hurried farewells.

What she said to me was that she no longer had anything here to stay here for, now that my father was dead. I don't recall that she said much of anything else. To me, that is. She said plenty of things to her friends. Of which, clearly, I no longer was one.

More fool me, I didn't figure that out for a long time. I actually sent my husband to Asheville to secretly check out the area, to see if we might want to move out there to stay closer to her. My mother had, after all, followed my grandmother here to Albuquerque, so it was sort of natural for me to consider closing the loop by following my mother back to the other side. It would have been appropriate, even anticipated. While he was out there, Jerry Garcia died. Paul reported back that Asheville was pretty cool but we would probably not want to move there right away. I didn't tell her we'd even given it thought.

WANTING TO KILL

It is the Fourth of July again, and this time we all go to visit: my husband and I, and Bob. It rains the entire time we are there, just rains and rains and rains. Being from New Mexico, I am unused to steady rainfall like this. I love it, but it depresses me. I have not brought enough clothing to deal with this much wet. None of us have. We buy umbrellas at a nearby shop. Later we go to discount store and Bob buys a little waterproof windbreaker. He's astonished at the low prices – Bob doesn't generally shop at discount stores. I warn him he will get what he pays for, and his windbreaker will likely last only a few months before it falls apart. I don't know if he believes me. My mother's stuffed dog has vanished so Bob picks up a new dog for her. This one has a huge, toothy smile. I think it looks ridiculous, but when we give it to her, she adores it. All she talks about for the rest of the visit is that dog with the teeth. "Look at these teeth, Cass. Just look at them! Teeth! Do you see these teeth?" Bob takes a picture of her with the dog. It's one of the last memories I will have of her.

Bob wants to do the Firecracker marathon again, so we all register for it. The marathon is not in Asheville, but in nearby Brevard, the quaint little mountain town Steve Martin sometimes calls home. They have white squirrels, we are told. I never see any of them. Bob wins a medal for his age group. I come in dead last for mine, which is unsurprising. I hate competitions, and I was walking pretty slow. On the drive back to Asheville, many of the roads have been washed out by the rain.

We have stayed this time at the Marriott, because they have a rooftop fireworks display. When we go to the viewing area, a single woman has laid claim to fully a quarter of the space, saying her friends are coming any moment, that they are right behind her on the next elevator. Seating is very limited, so we end up having to stand for quite a while. She shoos off dozens of people. Her friends never materialize.

On the last day we are there, during the last visit I will ever have with my mother, she tells me she *loves* the dog we gave her. She tells me the teeth are great and make her very happy. "But also," she says with sincerity, "they make me want to *kill*."

All I can do is nod. I tell her I feel the same way.

DEVOLUTION

Once she and Lorenzo moved to Asheville, with a wine store within walking distance, my mother's drinking ran absolutely amok. Lorenzo the enabler even started making wine in the basement, under the guise of saving money. When Uncle Bob went to visit, he reported back on an increasingly incoherent sister, face down in her salad at lunch. And she became more and more abusive. Yelling at me on the phone, demanding I send her gifts, complaining that I was a billionaire who would not buy her things, that I never visited and rarely called. Yelling at me for the gifts I did send.

One year I sent her a picture of a fish for Mother's day (a Mother's day cod) and another picture of a fish for her birthday (a Birthday cod) and then for Christmas had (at some expense) an entire cod dinner delivered to her house, with a note that read "Money's short, times are hard, here's your fucking Christmas Cod." This – the entire setup, the punchline, the whole affair – was a thing that would have made her laugh for hours once upon a time. What I got for my efforts was... nothing. So I called, to see if she had gotten the cod. "Yes, of course I got the fucking fish, Cass. Thanks. We ate it. It was fine. Billionaire daughter, sends me a fucking fish. I would have preferred the cash."

I lost my job shortly after that, so she never got another expensive fish, I can tell you that much.

BARBARA GOES DOWNHILL

My mother takes a turn for the worse just before my birthday. I am sure if someone will only tell her it IS my birthday, she will happily drop dead. She would have *loved* to die on my birthday. She called me when my great uncle Seldon died, to tell me he died on my birthday. She called me on my birthday three years in a row to remind me about Seldon. She later told me her dog died on my birthday, too. I don't know if any of it is true.

NUMEROUS ENEMIES

Lorenzo stayed in Asheville for only a few years. He then fled, leaving my mother to her own devices. My husband and I found that out when he rang our Albuquerque doorbell and handed us a bag of oranges. He told us he had moved to Florida because my mother tried to set fire to him when he said he wanted to go to his sister's funeral.

We were exhorted not to tell her where he was, nor to give her his number. And we didn't, of course, though I don't think she even thought to ask us. She wasn't making very much sense already.

After Lorenzo left, Barbara became convinced her brother had convinced him to go. She also became convinced Bob had arranged to have her brakes tampered with. When she – driving drunk through the Asheville tunnel – failed to stop in time and crashed her car, this was her excuse. Apparently police were not involved in that. But she did pop up on their radar at some point. A mere few months after Lorenzo left, her neighbors notified us the police had picked her up and taken her to a mental hospital because she was wandering around in the streets, acting bonkers. Because my mother was slick, she was able to convince them it was all a simple error. The medical director released her almost right away.

And that's when Bob became the enemy for real. Because he contacted them, gave them her history, and persuaded them they had made a mistake – and they picked her up again and committed her involuntarily for two weeks.

I was, unfortunately, still in what one could call her good graces. I joked with Bob that I wished I had called the cops on her and had her committed, because then she might leave me alone. Instead I was treated to a great number of drunken phone calls at all hours of the day and night: How evil Bob was, how evil Lorenzo was, how sexy Derrick was. How the house was falling apart at the seams, how her teeth were failing, how she needed chile. How broke, how endlessly terribly broke she was, starving right to death. Meals on Wheels brought food which she gave the dog, it was that dreadful. But oh thank goodness they did bring it, because the dog needed every scrap. And of course, how wonderful I was, always followed by how horrible. These phone calls rarely ended well.

STRAWS

Late in May of 2008, I mailed my mother a birthday present. It was not a cod, but a book and a box of green chiles in cans (which she had been demanding repeatedly over the previous few years – no green chile in any form available in North Carolina). Because it was costing a ridiculous amount to send the inferior canned chile, I had hit upon the idea of sending fresh whole ones, unroasted, so I had included three of these in her gift box. So when she called, I answered the phone in good cheer. I was looking forward to hearing whether they had arrived safely. I was looking forward to hearing how she was going to roast them and eat them. I was looking forward to the demand, the inevitable demand, for more.

But when I asked if she had gotten the package, she called me an idiot. Of course she had gotten it, why would she not have gotten it? I asked if she liked the gifts and she told me Derrick had put them in the basement and she could not get to them. Then she asked me who I was voting for in the primary and called me an idiot again when I said I was torn between Clinton and Obama. (You *have* to vote for Obama, Cass, don't be an idiot. You have a black *brother*, remember. Obama is the best one. Plus he's gorgeous, vote for Obama, don't be a dumbass.)

When I asked about the fresh chile, was it actually in the basement or...? Well, of course it is, where else would it be, Derrick took it all down there for me. But would she be able to roast the chile, because the idea – Cass of course I know how to roast chile, don't be so stupid, you're so stupid, thinking I won't know how to roast chile, I've been roasting chile since before you were born, you moron, stupid kid sending me unroasted chile trying to save money on shipping like an idiot, billionaire asshole daughter refusing to send chile, refusing to vote for a black man, stupid racist dumbass kid, stupid idiot thinking I can walk down the stairs to get the boxes, trying to save money on shipping like a moron, sending me stupid books, why don't you send money, stupid asshole kid... This went on for a while, like a manic recording, ceaseless, breathless, senseless bile just pouring into my ear.

And what I'd like to say, what I would really like to say, was that *this* was the last straw. That I hung up on her and never ever spoke to her again. Because that was my full intent when I hung up on her: to never speak to her again. I was done. I reminded myself that she had warned me over and over as a child that she would become abusive if she started drinking. I reminded myself that her own advice was that when she did that, I must cut and run, run far away, and never look back. I reminded myself that she had told me I was too good to put up with an abusive parent. And I hung up the phone, and I said out loud to my husband, to the cat, to the walls, to myself, done done done.

I did in fact ignore her calls after that. My husband answered a few of them, which annoyed me. God knows what she was saying to him. But I ignored her calls for months – many months, and many, many calls. I ignored them all.

And so, when my mother broke her hip about a year later, I did not know about it. She did try to call, but I didn't answer. I assumed she was calling to verbally abuse me, as she had done the prior year. But that friend of hers, Brett – he called me and said she'd called *him* on her birthday and told him she just broke her hip two days previous. He wanted to know wasn't I worried and wasn't I going to, like... DO something... and I said: she called you from her house on her birthday, drunk, to tell you she had broken her hip two days ago, and was already out of the hospital? Bullshit. She's making it up.

That's what I said. And it was what I believed. Firmly. (Until I saw her when I went to rescue her, and it was obvious that she had indeed suffered from a broken hip which had not been treated.)

After I stopped answering her calls, it took a while for her to get the idea, to grasp that it wasn't that I was never home, but that I was intentionally not answering the phone. Her calls slowed, then stopped entirely. Then she sent emissaries. Floy mailed me a letter, telling me how *special* I was (underlined) and how my mother needed me. Floy mailed me my mother's phone number.

I took the bait, which I regret doing, because it did not help matters any for me to try again, and because it made me feel weak to cave in. But I did try again, like a fool. Because of my genuine love and admiration for Floy, and my misguided certainty that she understood the situation well and wouldn't be blowing smoke up my ass about the desperate need for me to call Barbara, I tried again. After having not spoken to my mother for about a year, I called her (new) phone number. What I got for my efforts was the familiar nonsense, but with a new set of nonsense mixed in: I was a moron, and Derrick was her real son. I was not as good as Derrick, who was selling her his car, and he was so handsome, so gorgeous, and would I not, please, be so kind as to send more chile, (you stupid asshole kid of mine), because all the chile you sent a year ago is in the basement and did you know Derrick is selling me his car? She talked about nothing but Derrick and his car, and how handsome he was, and how stupid I was, and how she needed chile, for fifteen minutes straight. I thought (and think to this day) it was quite possible he had gotten her hooked on meth. She sounded like a speed freak.

And about that hip? Oh, yes, yes, I broke my hip last year, I did, and Derrick got me out of the hospital immediately because they were going to do a bunch of worthless operations and I hate doctors, he knows I hate doctors, he came and got me, and did you know he's selling me his car? Well he is, because mine doesn't work after Bob had the brakes tampered with, Derrick is my only true friend, my real son, unlike you, worthless bitch who won't send chile but will you please send me more chile because mine is in the basement and Derrick is selling me his car, he's so amazing, he's so smart and sexy and you're such a stupid bitch...

And that, well, that was really the last straw. I did not call again, nor did I answer any further phone calls from her. And that time, I kept my word: I did not speak to her again until the day I saw her at the nursing home, where her darling Derrick had left her.

Brett called often to update me: she had told him he could not visit during a certain week because she had family in town. When he inquired further about this he was told they were blood relatives she had not seen in a long time, named Mac and Delphi. (She had no such relatives.) Mac and Delphi, she told him, were her closest friends and really understood her. I assumed they were drunks she had met on the street. Her house was full of flies he said. The Council on Aging was concerned, he said. Derrick seemed to be moving in, he said. Would I not do something, he asked? What could I do? I replied. I told him about my childhood. I told him about everything. I do not think he believed me. About any of it. About literally any of it. Her helplessness was obvious, her dire straits commanding; my refusal to join in and offer succor, confusing. How could I turn my back?

But, dammit. How could I *not*? Having made the choice to turn away, I was serious about it. I wasn't being pulled in again, not for any reason. There's a thing about last straws: their very existence implies the existence of a number of previous straws, perhaps a vast quantity of them. Pages and pages.

Brett told me he overheard her telling some unknown entity over the phone that she had almost 80k in the bank and was quite well-set financially. That was actually true, but I didn't know it at the time. She'd told me some years previous that she was too broke to turn on the heat, and that if it weren't for her dog she would have frozen to death. She had said, between bouts of drunken shrieking, that she was afraid she would be frostbitten.

So despite what was (in retrospect) obviously about to happen, I said no. Over and over, I said no. And then the obvious thing happened: Derrick moved in, took all her money, had her sign a will naming him as her sole heir, moved her to a nursing home, and left her there to die.

And that time, when Brett called, I finally had to say yes. Yes, ok, I will come. To rescue Barbara.

NOVEMBER AND DECEMBER, COLD AND COLDER

In November, Bob goes again to visit my mother, this time without us. We have been told her death is imminent. Bob takes a picture of her and emails it to me. I will find out later he did that because he knows the funeral home will require a recent picture. I had no idea.

In December, the hospice workers call me and tell me she has a serious bladder infection. They will treat it if I request that, but it is my call. I tell them not to treat it. My mother dies a few days later. I am very relieved and angry and hurt and furious and everything I can be, all at once. Probably most daughters would have shame or guilt over that final call, but I don't. I am *glad* to give the order that kills her in the end. It is her own fault. All of this, every bit of this, was her own fault. None of it had anything to do with me. Brett was her last visitor. He says he told her it was ok to let go.

We've already arranged with a local funeral parlor to collect her upon her death and cremate her cheaply. For some reason, the hospice people have her body sent to the wrong funeral parlor. It takes a while to sort that out. Then the correct funeral parlor sends a bill, which I pay. I wait for her ashes, and I wait. I wait and wait. After a couple of weeks, I call them: where is my mother? They are holding her ashes because they failed to bill me for mailing them. I pay over the phone and receive her in the mail a few days later.

My mother arrives in a plastic box. At last, she has been rescued. We take her ashes to the corner of the land where I grew up, the house where she was last known by me to be sober and sensible. The place where I think she left her sanity: that's the place I scatter her ashes. On the land where she once rode horses. Near the home where she discovered that motherhood was not really her bag, I release her from it. She is free to roam the ditch bank there, La Llorona, the weeping woman.

I don't feel like putting up a Christmas tree that year. Who have I to impress with bows and ribbons?

SNOW ANGELS

When I was a child, it never snowed. Not in any meaningful amount, anyway; not enough to make snowmen, not enough for a snowball fight. In the wooded New Mexico valley where I grew up it just never seemed to happen. We were near the river, and something about the air currents prevented snowfall at my house, swept the rare clouds away just as they approached.

And then one day, it snowed. Real snow, huge vast whitenesses of it, and my mother called me to look out the window, and I was in awe. I was maybe six or seven years old. I opened the door and stood on the porch and listened to it falling, the quiet ticking of the snow against the hundreds of trees around me; listening to the soft *foomp* it made when branches let go and dropped mounds of snow onto the land beneath. These new sounds gave me goosebumps of excitement, but the one that really made the hairs stand up on the back of my neck was the no-sound of silence; the normally noisy, rustling bosque muffled by blankets of snow. It was like a movie, like a fairy tale. It was like anything could happen.

My mother, watching me, sighed. "Ok, Cass. Get your coat." She turned to put her own coat on. "There's something we have to do."

We pulled on boots and coats and tromped out into the snow, my mother sighing and muttering all the while, shaking her head. This march into the snow. This horrid chore.

She was taking me to make snow angels. I had never made them before, having been deprived of snow my whole young life.

Down the ditch bank a ways, at a clearing in the woods near the house, she selected an open spot. "This is good. Here. Now, lie down in the snow." She pointed. "Over there. Just lie there with your arms at your sides. Lie still." When I was lying in the snow, tickled and confused and thinking she had finally lost her mind as she had always said would happen, she lay nearby. "Now, move your arms and legs. Like this."

She demonstrated, and I copied her. A pair of snow angels were born, mother and daughter. We stood and leaped clear of them, then turned to view our handiwork.

They were beautiful, and I turned to tell her so, but she was already moving away, chore done. Going in, inside to dry off. The time for play was over.

"You had never seen snow like this, so I thought I better show you how to make snow angels," she said. "Now you can say you got to make them. When I was a kid, we made them all the time. It snowed a lot where I grew up. But you... well, enjoy it while it lasts; it may never happen again."

She took off her coat and nestled herself back on her couch, back with the book she had been reading, and she was gone. It really had been a distasteful chore to her, an obligation. *I must feed my child broccoli, I must teach her to clean her room. I must show her how a snow angel is made.* The rites of passage. I picture her with a list: Tooth under pillow, check. First day of school, check. Snow Angel, check. For her a chore, and for me a memory, still strong enough today to bring tears to my eyes. I remember everything about it so vividly: her new khaki parka with the little fringe of fake rabbit fur, my own red coat, how the cold snow smelled under the trees when we threw our arms and legs wide and stroked the earth with them. The view of our house as we walked up the snow-covered path, and the way the smoke from the fireplace made me feel guilty for polluting the air even as I inhaled the fragrance and loved it.

The next time it snowed, really snowed like that, it was another house and I was in my early teens. Immediately, I wanted to rush out and make snow angels with my mother, but she did not want to go, and she talked me out of going, as well. Dirty, cold, wet snow. What would be the point? I sat and watched the snow from the window instead, not yet knowing you can never go back.

* * * * *

Acknowledgements

I would like to thank my husband Paul and my uncle Bob. I could not have attempted the rescue without them; their patience and kindness is admirable. I would also like to thank 'Brett' for staying in touch even when I refused to cooperate, and for finding her and forcing the rescue attempt I so badly did not want to make. If I hadn't tried, I wouldn't have known it was impossible, and I might have blamed myself for the losses that were, in fact, inevitable. Anything that keeps me from beating myself up is always, always, appreciated.

Cass J McMain

GRINGO

You don't have to die to become a ghost.

Daniel lives alone, and he does nothing but sleep and work, work and sleep. When this sleep is repeatedly interrupted by his neighbor's barking dog, he surprises himself by doing something despicable. When he finally meets the mysterious neighbor, he surprises himself again: he finds that a friend is something he's been missing more than he knew.

Ellie's been having a very rough time since tragedy struck her family. Her out-of-state brother wants to move her into a nursing home as soon as they can sell her old house. But it needs a lot of work, and she just hasn't been able to deal with it alone.

As the year goes by Daniel and Ellie come to rely on each other more and more. But time does not stand still, even though Ellie insists that it does, and Daniel discovers he is in the midst of huge changes –and has been there for some time. In fact he, and Ellie –and Gringo –have been somewhere pretty unexpected all along.

Gringo is a novel about time, and the way it marches on –or doesn't, as the case may be.

Cass J McMain

WATCH

Before he knew about the bruises, he knew about the cheating. And before he knew about the cheating, he knew about the blood. He'd seen Edgar with blood on his hands before, after all. But there had been more and more of it –and Edgar had seemed less and less concerned about hiding it...
Some people inherit the strangest things.

Corky inherits her Uncle Moony's diary, she finds he had a strange and frightening obsession about his brother... a brother with his own disturbing practices. Moony watched Edgar as though his life depended on it. Edgar watched his brother right back. But Edgar disappeared, and now nobody has seen him for years.

Corky can't decide which one was crazier. Now that Moony is gone, who will be forced to take up the next watch, and who will be watched? What has she really inherited?
Not about vampires; though that isn't quite certain. Certainly old Moony thought his brother was vampired. His niece is intrigued, and maybe tempted...

A scintillating, beautiful novel about difference, suspicion, and acceptance of one's own nature.

Cass J McMain

SUNFLOWER

Michael is a metalworker with a name for building good fences. He's even known by some neighborhood kids as Mr. Fence Man. But he wants to be something more: an artist like his former business partner, Alex. An artist, like his girlfriend, Jess, wants him to be. The commissions are starting to come in, and along with steady work making fences, things are looking good. The only problem he has is with his closest neighbor, who won't allow visitors to pass through a gate between their properties. This dispute becomes a fight and Michael, enraged, makes a wrong choice.

Haunted by the result of his choice, Michael starts to fall apart: a death weighs down on him, exposing the weaknesses in the persona he was creating for himself, the weaknesses at the heart of him.

Sunflower is a story about a man having a bad day and making one bad choice. But underneath that, it is also about his coming to terms with himself: who he is - and who he is not. Ultimately, Sunflower is about how we define ourselves as people, and how we seek to be what we are not.

An extraordinary and beautiful novel.

About the Author...

Cass J McMain was born in Albuquerque and raised in the far North Valley, among the cottonwoods. Her first love was always houseplants, and she now maintains a house full of them.

Her background as a greenhouse manager led to a long career in garden center management, but when the bottom fell out of the local industry, she took a new path. Or rather, an old path; Cass started writing at the age of six, knocking out stories on her typewriter.

While her love of nature came in part from her father, a man with the heart of a farmer and the soul of a philosopher, much of the writing Cass did as a child was done to please her mother, a woman with the heart of a philosopher, the soul of a demon and the unquenchable thirst of the mind reserved for the brilliant.

Recently, Cass's writing muse has again been speaking to her: a voice she stopped paying attention to a long time ago. Her plants, some of which she has had since she was nine years old, remain the heart of her life, but now she has a desire to express herself in other ways.

Bowed, but not broken, Cass keeps her eye on the horizon, looking for a greenhouse to manage. Her favourite saying these days is "that was then; this is now."